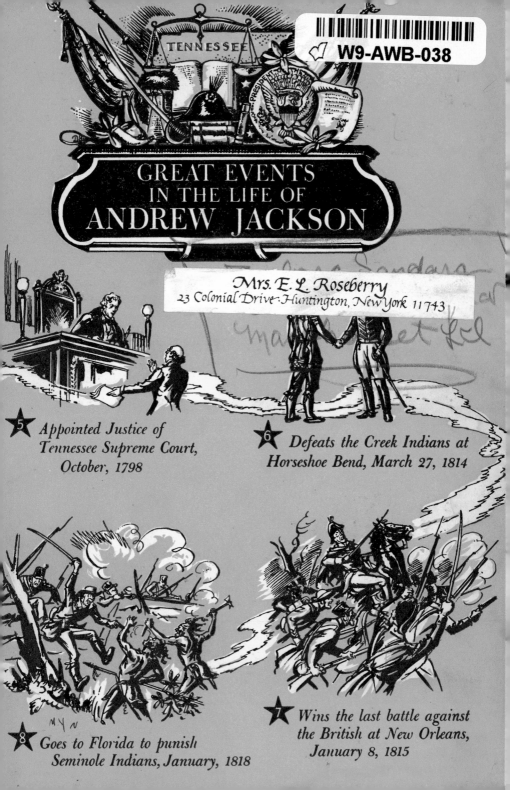

GREAT EVENTS
IN THE LIFE OF
ANDREW JACKSON

5 Appointed Justice of
Tennessee Supreme Court,
October, 1798

6 Defeats the Creek Indians at
Horseshoe Bend, March 27, 1814

8 Goes to Florida to punish
Seminole Indians, January, 1818

7 Wins the last battle against
the British at New Orleans,
January 8, 1815

THE STORY OF
Andrew Jackson

"He more than any one else of his day threw the task of judging upon the common man. And this he did without cant and in entire sincerity. No passionate dreamer of the past was more willing than he to test his principles to the uttermost."
—JOHN SPENCER BASSETT

He was breathless but he gasped out his strange story

THE STORY OF
Andrew Jackson

By ENID LAMONTE MEADOWCROFT

Illustrated by DAVID HENDRICKSON

PUBLISHERS Grosset & Dunlap NEW YORK

With love to my sister
JEAN LAMONT

PRINTED IN THE UNITED STATES OF AMERICA

Library of Congress Catalog Card No. 52–13742

Contents

[*v*]

Illustrations

[*vii*]

THE STORY OF
Andrew Jackson

Andy sprang before the word was finished

CHAPTER ONE

"I'll Never Stay Throwed"

ANDY JACKSON dropped his fishing pole by the roadside. His freckled face was scarlet. His blue eyes blazed with anger. Clenching his fists, he turned on the boy who stood near by.

"Just call my Uncle James that name again!" he cried hotly. "Say it again! I dare you!"

George McWhorter chuckled. "I didn't mean it, Andy," he said good-naturedly. "I was only trying to get your temper up. You get mad so quick and—"

"Say it again!" Andy commanded, with his eyes still blazing.

George smiled and shrugged his shoulders.

"All right, you little red-headed rooster," he replied, bracing himself. "If you want to fight —I said your Uncle James was a Tor—!"

Andy sprang before the word was finished. The boys came together like two young bulls. Fists flew. Bare feet lashed out. Red dust rose in a cloud as the boys clinched and each one struggled to throw the other down.

Andy was using all his strength. But a nine-year-old is seldom a match for a boy who is nearly twelve. Before he knew how it happened, Andy was flat on his back, blinking up at the hot August sun. And George was kneeling astride his chest, pinning him down by the shoulders.

Both boys were breathing heavily. But George was laughing.

"You—fight pretty good—for such a skinny little—rooster," he panted. "But you'd ought to know better than—to tackle a—big fellow like me. Had enough?"

Andy shook his head. Squirming and twisting, he tried to get away. George held him firmly and laughed again.

[*4*]

"I don't want to hurt you, Andy," he declared. "I was just trying to get you mad.

"Of course your Uncle James ain't a Tory. He's on our side in the war. Not on England's. And everybody here in the Waxhaws knows it. There! Now will you say you've had enough, so's I can let you up?"

Andy grinned. He wasn't angry any more, for he now had no reason to be. But he wouldn't say he was beaten, either. For a moment he lay perfectly still.

Without thinking, George had loosened his hold on the younger boy's shoulders. Suddenly, Andy shoved him to one side. Turning over quickly, he started to scramble up to his feet.

"No, you don't!" George cried. Grabbing him around the knees, he threw him down with a thud. Then he sat on him heavily.

"What's the matter with you, anyway?" he asked as Andy struggled to get up. "I throw you fair, but you don't *stay* throwed."

Andy grinned sheepishly. "There's something takes—hold of me—when I'm—down,"

[5]

he replied, still struggling. "I reckon—I'll never—stay throwed. Not by you or—anybody else."

Straining every muscle, he humped up his body and tried to throw George off. But at that very moment, George jumped up hastily.

"Look out!" he warned. "There's a wagon train a-coming. You'd better get up."

Andy scrambled to his feet and stepped to the roadside. Together he and George watched the wagons which were rolling toward them. Each wagon was covered with a white canvas hood and pulled by four strong horses. Andy counted the wagons as they rumbled by.

"There are twelve of them," he announced, hitching up his brown pantaloons. "Big ones, too."

"They're carrying grain up north to General Washington's army," George added.

Andy nodded and watched the last wagon disappear around the bend in the road. He knew where that wagon train was going just as well as George did. He knew about General

Washington's army, too. And why many people in the thirteen American colonies were at war with England.

It was because the King of England had been treating them so badly. Making stupid laws for them. Ordering them to pay taxes which were not fair. And sending red-coated soldiers across the ocean to force the Americans to obey him.

This had made many Americans furious. And so the war had started. Already there had been two hard-fought battles in colonies far to the north of the Waxhaws. The English had also tried to capture Charleston, to the south. But they had not succeeded. And no English soldiers had yet pushed their way into South Carolina.

"I just wish some of them *would* come here!" Andy suddenly exclaimed aloud. "We'd take good care of them!"

George looked at him in surprise. "Wish who'd come?" he asked.

"Redcoats," Andy replied, slapping at a mosquito which was buzzing near his ear. "I'll pop them off like rabbits if I ever get a chance. Soon as I'm big enough I'm going to join the militia."

"So am I," George declared. "I aim to be a major when I grow up, like your Uncle Robert. My pa says he's the bravest man around here."

Andy grinned. "He's the richest, too," he boasted. "There isn't anybody in the Wax-haws that's got a house as big as my Uncle Robert's."

He crossed the road and picked up his fish-

ing pole. George followed him, scuffing his bare feet in the dust.

"If I was you, Andy, I'd live with your Uncle Robert, instead of living with your Uncle James," he said. "Why don't you?"

"Don't want to," Andy replied quickly. "That's why. My mother took my brothers to Uncle James' house when my father died. And that's where I was born, and I like it there. So do Mother and Rob and Hugh. Are you going home now?"

George glanced at the sun. "Yep, it's 'most milking time," he said. "Where are you going?"

"Home," Andy replied. "I'll see you tomorrow, maybe." And, whistling loudly, he set off down the road.

It did not take him long to reach the big farm which belonged to his uncle, James Crawford. Still whistling, he turned up the lane which led to the house.

It was a large, comfortable-looking log house, standing on a low grassy hill. In a field beyond the house, Andy saw his Uncle James pitching hay. Three of Uncle James' sons were helping him.

One of them waved an arm at Andy. Andy waved back. He stooped to pat a big brown dog which had come to meet him.

"Come on, Rover," he said. And with the dog at his heels, he ran around the house. Dropping his fishing pole near the back steps, he went into the kitchen.

Though the windows were open, the room was filled with the smell of cooking. Chicken stew bubbled in the big iron pot which hung over the fire. And his mother was setting the table for supper.

She put down a pile of pewter plates when she saw Andy.

"Where have you been all the afternoon?" she asked with a smile.

"Fishing," Andy replied, looking hungrily at a plate piled high with hot corn bread. "I didn't catch anything though, except a couple of crappies. And they were so little that I threw them back. Then coming home, I met George McWhorter and we got into a fight and—"

"Another fight!" Mrs. Jackson exclaimed. She sighed and gently pushed a lock of red hair back from the boy's eyes. "Andy, I wish you weren't so quick to use your fists," she went on soberly. "Learn to harness up your temper, son. Don't let it get the best of you. I want you to be a preacher when you grow up."

"A preacher!" Andy repeated in dismay. "You mean like Reverend Cummins?" He

[*11*]

shook his head quickly. "Why, I'd have to be good all the time!" he exclaimed. "I could never do that."

He looked so worried as he spoke, that his mother couldn't help laughing.

"You can try," she said, patting his shoulder. "Now go and wash your face and tie back your hair. You're a sight!"

She gave him a little push toward the door. Andy went outside. He splashed his face with some water from the bucket which stood on a bench near the step. Then he picked up the wooden comb lying beside the bucket and started to comb back his long hair. But he stopped suddenly with the comb in mid-air.

"Hey, Mother!" he cried, sticking his head through the door. "Here come Hugh and Rob a-running as if a bear was chasing them. Where've they been?"

"At your Uncle Robert's," Mrs. Jackson replied, stepping to the doorway. "Sake's alive! I hope nothing's wrong there!"

And she stared at the boys who were racing across the meadow toward the house.

CHAPTER TWO

Big News

HUGH reached the house first, for his legs were longer than Rob's. Puffing and panting, he sank down on the steps at his mother's feet.

"The—the post-rider's come!" he gasped as soon as he could speak. "He's brought a newspaper to Uncle Robert and—"

"There's big news!" Rob shouted as he raced across the yard. "It's about the war and—"

"Has there been another battle?" Mrs. Jackson broke in.

"Are the redcoats coming?" Andy asked eagerly.

Rob shook his head. "No, it's something else," he replied, still panting. "But—but I don't know what. Uncle Robert—wouldn't tell us."

"He's all stirred up about it, though," Hugh went on. "He says something's happened that will change our whole country and—"

"And he wants us to ride around and—tell folks that there'll be a public reading—at his house tonight " Rob added. "At seven o'clock. And he says Andy can be the reader, if he—wants to."

"Of course he does!" Mrs. Jackson exclaimed with a smile. "Don't you, Andy?"

"If I can go over to Uncle Robert's early and study out the hard words, I do," Andy replied promptly.

"You can go the minute you've put on a clean shirt and had your supper," his mother declared. "I'll dish out some stew for you right away. You boys had better get started if you're going to invite folks to a seven o'clock reading. It's nearly five now."

Hugh nodded and stood up. "I'll saddle Blackie and Nell while Rob goes to the hay field to tell Uncle James about it," he said.

He started immediately for the barn. Rob ran off toward the hay field. And Andy followed his mother into the house.

It was always an exciting day for the Waxhaws people when the post-rider galloped into their little settlement. He came only once a month, from Charleston, one hundred and fifty miles away. In his saddle bags he brought letters and newspapers which told how the war was going.

[15]

These papers were expensive. Few people in the Waxhaws could afford to subscribe to them. So every month Major Crawford invited friends and neighbors to his house, to hear the news read aloud.

Often he read to them, himself, or asked another man to do it. But now and then he chose Andy to be the public reader. For already the boy could read better than either of his brothers, though Rob was eleven and Hugh was two years older. Indeed, Andy could read almost as well as any grown person in the settlement.

This made Mrs. Jackson very proud. But she did not speak of it as she talked with her neighbors on Major Crawford's porch that evening. Sitting down in a low chair, she looked around at the people who had come to hear the news.

Men in rough farm clothes and men in knee breeches and neat jackets stood talking together in little groups. Women with babies in their arms and women without babies had found seats on the porch or the steps. Boys and girls played under the trees, or romped on the grass while they waited for the reading to begin.

Mr. Humphries, the schoolteacher, was there in his long black coat and his freshly powdered wig. Old Nick Sands was stumping up the path on his wooden peg leg. And John Thompson, who lived on Cain Creek, ten miles away, was just helping his wife get off her horse.

"There must be 'most forty folks here," Mrs. Jackson remarked to Uncle James, who sat beside her.

"Aye, near everyone in the settlement's come," Uncle James declared, puffing on his long clay pipe. "Rob and Hugh spread the word fast. I hope our Andy reads out good and strong."

"I hope the news he reads is good news," Mrs. Jackson said anxiously. "Maybe this dreadful war will be over soon. Look! Here comes your brother with Andy now."

And there was Major Crawford in his fine

[*17*]

blue uniform, standing in the doorway with Andy beside him. A hush fell over the little crowd when the Major stepped forward.

"The newspaper we have today was printed far away in Philadelphia, friends," he said loudly. "The Congress has met there again.

And they have made a declaration which will
mean great things for our country. If you'll
gather closer so that all can hear well, young
Andrew Jackson will read it."

There was a buzz of talking as people
moved nearer to the porch. Andy stepped onto
a little bench which stood near the door.

His tongue felt thick and his lips were dry.
Though he had studied the hard words again
and again, he was afraid he might stumble
over some of them. But he planted his feet

firmly on the bench. And his hands were steady as he held the newspaper up to catch the light of the setting sun.

Clearing his throat, he looked over the edge of the paper at his mother. She smiled at him and nodded encouragingly. In a loud, shrill voice Andy began to read.

"In Congress, July 4, 1776. The unanimous declaration of the thirteen united states of America. When in the course—"

"Hey, wait a minute!" Nick Sands shouted from the edge of the crowd. "What's this about states? We ain't states! We're colonies! English colonies!"

"Not any more," Major Crawford called back. "This is a declaration of independence. Keep quiet now and listen. Go on, Andy."

So Andy went on. He did not understand all that he was reading. But something about the words filled him with pride. And his voice rang out, clear as a bell, right through the very last line of the long declaration.

No one stirred for a moment after he had finished. Then Dan Hart, the blacksmith, scratched his head.

"Them's good fancy words that Andy's been reading," he cried. "But what in all tarnation do they mean?"

"They mean we're through with taking orders from King George," young Bill Wrenn shouted excitedly. "We ain't going to be ruled by him any more! Nor by England, either!"

"We're not going to be ruled by *anyone!*" Mr. Humphries declared loudly. "We're going to run our own country now. We're states. Free and independent states!"

"United states!" Uncle James boomed in his deep voice.

"Aye, but we've got to lick the redcoats before we really get to be free and independent!" cried a man with a stubby black beard.

"Don't you worry about that, McKemy," Major Crawford called back. "We'll lick them if it takes us a hundred years."

"Hurray!" Andy cried excitedly, waving the newspaper over his head. Then he flushed, feeling that he had sounded very foolish.

But others took up the cry.

"Hurray for the American states!"

"United States!"

"Hurray! Hurray! Hurray!"

The shouting frightened one of the babies, who began to cry lustily. And everybody started to talk at once. Andy looked inquiringly at his Uncle Robert.

"Shall I read anything else?" he asked.

"No," replied Major Crawford, taking the paper from the boy. "We've heard the important news. It's the most important news that has ever come to the Waxhaws, Andy. Some day you'll be proud that you read it to us."

Andy nodded and jumped down from the bench. He had read so long and cheered so loudly that his throat felt scratchy.

"You're hoarse as an old crow," Rob told him as everyone started home.

"I don't care," Andy croaked. "I just wish I could fly like a crow!"

"Why?" Hugh asked curiously. "Where would you go?"

"Off to fight redcoats," Andy replied. And he ran ahead to catch up with his mother, who was walking with Uncle James and his sons Joe, and Bill, and Jim.

They were all talking together about the Declaration of Independence and what it would mean to the country. Andy listened for almost a minute, waiting impatiently for a chance to speak. Then he broke in abruptly.

"Uncle James, when will the war get here to the Waxhaws?" he asked eagerly.

"Never, I hope," Uncle James replied, putting his hand on the boy's shoulder. "We're a long way from any big town, Andy. I don't believe British soldiers will ever come here."

But the British did come to the Waxhaws, though it took them many months to get there. And when they came they brought suffering and unhappiness to many of the Waxhaws people. Among them was young Andy Jackson.

CHAPTER THREE

A Plan for Andy

ANDEE! An-dee! Andy Jackson!"

Mrs. Jackson stood in the kitchen doorway, shading her eyes from the early March sun.

"Andy!" she called again, stepping outside. "You get off that crazy colt before she throws you, and come to breakfast this minute."

Andy turned the colt around and brought her up short.

"Pixie's not going to throw me," he shouted gaily. "Watch me take her over the fence."

He leaned low on Pixie's back. Pounding her sides with his heels, he raced her across the pasture. At that moment Hugh and Robert and the three Crawford boys came crowding to the kitchen doorway.

[*24*]

"Little fool!" Bill muttered, looking over Hugh's shoulder at Andy. "He'll get himself hurt, sure as shooting! That Pixie's the meanest colt I ever—"

He stopped speaking abruptly and Mrs. Jackson caught her breath. For Andy and Pixie were nearing the fence.

"Here we go!" shouted Andy. And the colt jumped. She cleared the top rail gracefully.

"Good work!" Rob shouted.

Mrs. Jackson sighed with relief and Jim

Crawford chuckled. He spoke to his father, who had just stepped up behind him.

"That young one knows more about horses than any of us," he remarked. "He can handle them, no matter how mean they are."

"He rides better than most boys of eleven." Uncle James agreed.

"Andy!" Mrs. Jackson called. "Get that colt back to the pasture, and hurry up about it. You'll be late to school if you don't."

Andy glanced at the sky and whistled under his breath. The sun said it was past seven o'clock. School was held in the Waxhaws meeting house, nearly five miles away. And Mr. Humphries sometimes used his birch rod on boys who were late.

"I'll hurry!" he cried. And he galloped toward the pasture. Soon he was seated at the breakfast table in the kitchen, with the rest of the family.

There was little conversation as everyone devoured eggs, ham, fried hominy, and corn bread spread with honey. Then Uncle James poured himself a second cup of coffee and began to talk about the war. And about the British, who had captured the city of Philadelphia.

"They've been there all winter, and I hear they've had an easy time of it," Uncle James said soberly. "But George Washington and his men have been near starving in a little place called Valley Forge. If things don't go better for our side soon—"

He shook his head. Wiping his mouth on the back of his hand, he pushed his chair from the table and clumped from the kitchen. A moment later the Crawford boys followed him out to the fields. Hugh and Rob went off to do their chores. And Andy was left alone with his mother.

She wrapped up some corn bread, an apple, and a thick slice of ham for his lunch. As she handed him the packet of food, she looked at him soberly.

"Mr. Humphries stopped your uncle after militia meeting last night," she said, "to talk about you. He says you're troublesome in school this year, Andy. That you're noisy and don't keep your mind on your lessons."

Andy's face reddened under his freckles. "Well, I try to," he said, rubbing one bare foot against another, "but—"

"No excuses, now," his mother broke in, brushing some crumbs from his jacket. "I expect you to be the best scholar in the Waxhaws. You're smart enough. I want you to try harder."

"I will," Andy promised, with a quick smile. "Honest, I will."

And he remembered that promise for two whole days. But on the third day he forgot. It was after dark when he raced home and pushed open the kitchen door.

Supper was over. Rob sat at the table, cleaning his rifle by candlelight. And Mrs. Jackson was spinning near the fire.

She looked around anxiously when Andy burst into the room. Then she gasped.

The boy's face was crimson. One of his eyes was black and swollen. There was blood on his brown homespun jacket, and his pantaloons were torn.

"Andrew Jackson!" his mother exclaimed.

[28]

"What on earth have you been doing? And where have you been?"

"Old Humphries kept me a long time after school because I missed nine words in spelling," Andy replied, sitting down to take a stone out of his shoe. "Then I stopped to watch a cockfight down by the blacksmith shop. Dan Hart matched his little red rooster against Bill Wrenn's rooster, Tewky, and—"

"Who won?" Rob asked quickly.

"Tewky," Andy replied, putting on his shoe.

"I suppose Tewky gave you that black eye, too," his mother remarked, as she pushed aside her spinning wheel and stood up.

Andy laughed. "Oh, no!" he exclaimed, getting to his feet. "After the cockfight was over, some of us boys ran races and had a jumping match out back of McWhorters' barn. I ran faster and jumped higher than anyone else, but Tom Gray said he did, so—"

"So you tried to prove you were right by using your fists," his mother said quietly.

Andy nodded. "Tom's got two black eyes,"

[*29*]

he declared with a chuckle. "And I'm starving!"

"You can get your own supper," his mother told him. "There's milk in that pewter pitcher and bread in the cupboard. That's all you deserve when you get home so late."

There was a worried look in her eyes as she lighted another candle and went back to her spinning. Andy filled a mug with milk and put some bread on a plate. He sat down on the bench near Rob and began to eat hungrily. In low voices the boys discussed the cockfight

[*30*]

and made plans to go hunting the next morning.

At last Mrs. Jackson stopped her work and turned around in her chair.

"Andy," she said soberly, "it's time you settled down to your studies and I can see now

that you'll never do it here. I've been thinking about this for a long time. Next fall I'm going to send you to Reverend Cummins' boarding school. It's twenty miles away, so you'll have to live there. But there are nice boys in the school. And you'll learn Latin and Greek, and other things you'll need to know, before you can become a preacher."

At the word "preacher," Rob grinned.

"Andy's too wild to be a preacher, Mother," he protested, getting up to put away his rifle.

"No," said Mrs. Jackson firmly. "He's not. He can be anything he wants to be, if he just makes up his mind to it. How about it, Andy? What do you think of it all?"

Andy looked doubtful. He didn't want to be a preacher. And he wasn't sure he would like living with Reverend Cummins. But fall seemed a long way off. And he really did want to please his mother, for he loved her dearly.

"Well," he said slowly, "I'll go to Reverend Cummins' school if you say I must, and I'll try to work hard. But—but can I come home sometimes for a visit?"

"Of course," his mother exclaimed with a smile. And so the matter was settled.

CHAPTER FOUR

"The War Is Coming Closer"

YOUNG MATTHEW DAVIS leaned over Andy's bed. He shook the boy roughly by the shoulder.

"Wake up, Andy!" he said. "Mrs. Cummins rang the rising bell ten minutes ago. Do you want me to pour cold water on you?"

Andy grunted and shook his head sleepily. Climbing out of bed, he pulled on his breeches, and glanced around the big attic room. The six other boys who boarded with Reverend Cummins were nearly dressed. Quickly Andy slipped into his shirt.

He scrubbed his freckled face with a wet towel and braided his dark red hair into a neat queue. When the breakfast bell rang he clattered downstairs behind Matt and tall Jock Sanders.

Nearly seven months had passed since Andy Jackson had come to live with Reverend Cummins. They had been busy months. For Francis Cummins saw to it that his pupils worked hard at their studies.

Under the sharp eyes of the minister, Andy's spelling and grammar had greatly improved. The boy was doing well in arithmetic, too. And the only subject with which he had any real trouble was Latin.

He sighed deeply as he opened his brown paper copybook that afternoon. Mr. Cummins had given him ten Latin sentences to translate. When he had finished three, he stopped to rest. Chewing idly on his goose-quill pen, he stared out of the window, wishing he were at home, trapping muskrats with Rob.

Suddenly he remembered a paper which he had in his pocket. Matt Davis had given it to him at dinner time so that he could copy it.

"I might as well copy it now," Andy

thought, "and finish my Latin later." Turning to the back page of his exercise book, he began to write hastily:

A MEMORANDUM HOW TO FEED A COCK BEFORE YOU HIM FIGHT.

"Take and give him some Pickle Beaf cut fine 3 times a day and give him sweet Milk instead of water to Drink. give him Dry Indien Corn that hase been Dryn Up in smoke give him lighte wheat Bread Soked in sweet Milk. feed him as Much as he Can Eat for Eaight Days—

Suddenly Andy heard a snicker and his pen stopped racing over the page. He looked up quickly. All the boys were watching him. So was Reverend Cummins. There was a strange expression on the minister's face.

"Andrew," he said, "I've spoken to you twice and had no answer. You are writing your Latin exercise so rapidly that I am eager to see it. Please bring it here to me."

"But—but, sir," Andy stammered unhappily. "It's not—"

"Bring it here," the minister repeated.

"Yes, sir."

Slipping Matt's paper into his pocket, Andy stood up. He handed Reverend Cummins his open copybook. Then he eyed the minister's willow switch, wondering how soon he would feel its sharp sting on his legs.

Every other boy in the room was wondering, too. There was not a sound as Reverend Cummins settled his steel-rimmed spectacles on his nose and looked at the words Andy had set down.

"Hmm!" said the minister, closing the book. "I see you find cockfighting more interesting than Latin, eh, Andrew?"

"Yes, sir," Andy replied honestly. "I don't like Latin."

"However, you were sent here to learn it," Reverend Cummins remarked. "And I mean to see that you do."

He reached for his switch. But at that moment there was a sharp knock at the door. Mr. Cummins crossed the room quickly, opened the door, and spoke in low tones with the man who stood outside. Then he turned to the boys with a worried frown.

Reverend Cummins looked at the words
Andy had set down

"I've just received important news," he said quietly. "You all know that the British have captured Savannah, to the south of us. Now I learn that they have taken all of Georgia.

"The war is coming closer, lads, and I fear it is coming here. If it does, some of you may never have a chance to go to school again. So study while you can, and study hard."

He sat down heavily in his chair. To Andy's relief, he seemed to have forgotten about the switch. But he had not forgotten the Latin lesson. When school was over, he told Andy to remain in his seat, and worked with him until it was nearly dark. Then the minister closed his book.

"You see, Andrew," he said, "that you can learn quickly when you're interested. I wouldn't be surprised if you could do anything you really wanted to do. Maybe you'll do something important one day."

"I'm afraid it won't be preaching, sir!" Andy exclaimed, picking up his copybook. "I don't know just what I would be good at, but—"

[38]

He broke off suddenly.

"Sir," he said eagerly, "if those danged—I mean those redcoats—have got Georgia, they'll go for Charleston. And if they get Charleston, they'll head right here for the back country. Sir, if you'll let us boys drill like the militia, even with sticks, we'll—"

"You'll be ready for them?" asked Reverend Cummins with a little smile. "Well, Andrew, I think you have a good idea. You boys may start your drilling tomorrow."

So the next day, after school, the boys

drilled in the clearing before the house. And they fought mock battles, using sticks for guns. They soon made Andy their captain, for they found he was quick at planning new ways of attacking the enemy when they played war games. And there was something about the way he shouted commands that made them want to obey him.

One sunny afternoon early in May, Andy was drilling his young soldiers in the clearing.

"About face!" he shouted. "Company—"

Suddenly he stopped. "Company, fall out!" he cried excitedly. Then he ran to meet Rob, who was just riding up the path, leading an extra horse.

"Hey, what brings you here?" Andy asked anxiously as his brother dismounted. "Has anything gone wrong at home?"

Rob shook his head and lifted a pair of saddlebags from his horse's back. "Uncle Robert's just heard that the British are getting ready to attack Charleston," he said soberly. "Our militia's going there to fight them, and Hugh's going with them. Mother wants you to come home before he leaves."

"Do you mean Hugh's really going to war?" Andy asked, as though he couldn't believe his ears.

"Yes," Rob said, handing him the saddle-bags. "You'd better pack all your things in these, Andy. And say good-by to Reverend Cummins. The chances are that you won't be coming back."

Andy nodded slowly. All at once the war seemed very close and rather frightening. Without a word, he pushed past the boys who were gathering around Rob, and went into the house.

CHAPTER FIVE

Dangerous Times

IT WAS a warm afternoon in May a year later. Cattle grazed peacefully in Uncle James' pasture. Chickens scratched in the dusty yard. And old Rover lay sunning himself in the kitchen doorway.

Andy stepped around the dog and entered the kitchen. Swinging a heavy sack from his shoulder, he set it on the table with a thud.

"There," he said to his mother. "When that pewter's melted down it'll make enough bullets to kill a hundred redcoats. Mrs. Thompson sent all her pewter plates and Mrs. Dunlap sent three mugs, but Mrs. Johnson didn't send a thing. Do you think those Johnsons are Tories?"

"They'll bear watching," his mother replied. "Now go out and help Rob chop wood."

Andy nodded and left the room. A moment later his mother saw him start across the yard, holding his axe over his shoulder like a rifle.

"He walks like Hugh," she thought, and her eyes filled with tears. For young Hugh had died near Charleston, after fighting bravely in a battle at a place called Stono Ferry.

The Americans had defeated the British in that battle. But the redcoats had captured Charleston at last. Led by General Cornwallis and a cruel officer named Tarleton, they were now pushing farther into South Carolina. With the help of Tories, they were raiding

towns, burning houses and barns, stealing cattle, and killing or capturing hundreds of Americans who dared to defy them.

No one knew how soon the redcoats might reach the Waxhaws. But the men in the Waxhaws militia were determined to drive them back when they came. The militia men had joined another small band of Americans, and were now camping ten miles southeast of the settlement.

Of course Rob and Andy wanted to be with them. But Uncle Robert had said that both boys were still too young to join the army. And Uncle James had told them that they must run the farm and attend to all the chores while he and his sons were away.

"Chores!" Andy thought impatiently, as he began to chop up a log. "I just wish these logs were British soldiers. I'd fix them!"

He swung his axe up with such force that the axe head came off. It sailed through the air and landed near Rob's feet.

Andy went to pick up the axe head, which was partly buried in the ground. Suddenly his sharp ears caught the sound of thudding hoofs.

"Someone's coming, Rob, and coming fast!" he cried.

Dropping the handle of his axe, he ran around the house with Rob at his heels, just as George McWhorter came galloping up the lane. George's face was white and his eyes were as big as saucers.

"Tarleton's redcoats have attacked our militia!" he gasped, pulling up his foam-flecked horse. "They surprised our men in camp about two hours ago! Caught them off guard and—"

He stopped and drew a deep breath.

"And what?" Mrs. Jackson asked sharply, running up to the boys.

"Our men fought like wildcats, ma'am," George exclaimed. "But lots of them were killed before the redcoats left. And others were hurt bad. Those that can drive are bringing the wounded home in wagons. They're taking the ones that are hurt worst to the church."

He wheeled his horse around and galloped off to spread the dreadful news. For an instant the Jacksons stood perfectly still. Then Mrs. Jackson spoke quickly.

[45]

"Hitch one of the horses to the wagon at once, Andy," she commanded. "Rob, fetch all the blankets in the house. Sheets, too. We'll need them for bandages. We'll want buckets for water. And candles. Don't stand there gawking! We can't waste a minute!"

And they didn't! When the wounded arrived at the church at sundown, the Jacksons were waiting to help them. So were several women from the settlement.

Never did Andy forget his first sight of men who had been hurt in battle. Some were dying, even as they were being lifted from the wagons. Others moaned or cried out in pain as they were carried into the church.

The Crawford boys had all been wounded. But Uncle Robert had not been hurt. Neither had Uncle James, though both men had been in the thick of the fighting.

"They're digging graves for the dead," Jim Crawford said as Mrs. Jackson bound up a long deep gash in his leg. "Let Andy finish putting on that bandage, Aunt Betty. There's others worse off than I am. Take care of them."

*When the wounded arrived at the church, the
Jacksons were waiting to help them*

So Mrs. Jackson moved on to the next man. Andy kneeled down beside Jim. With trembling fingers, he finished his mother's work.

"War's awful," he whispered, watching Jim's blood seep through the layers of cloth.

"Yes," Jim replied, gritting his teeth as he tried to sit up. "War's terrible. But we're fighting for big things, Andy. Freedom and—"

"Someone bring water," Tige Wilson moaned softly. "Water! Water!"

Picking up a wooden water bucket, Andy hurried to his side. Gently he raised Tige's head and held a dripping dipper to his lips.

All through that terrible night, Andy and Rob helped nurse the wounded. A few of the men died before morning. Others died during the days that followed. The rest grew strong enough at last to go to their own homes.

Meanwhile, all the men in the Waxhaws militia who were able to travel had gone to North Carolina. For there, not far from the settlement, a large force of Americans was gathering to march against the British.

Except in Tory families, the Waxhaws people now waited uneasily, day after day, praying that the redcoats would not come to their settlement. But they came, one June morning.

There was only a small band of them, and they did not come to fight. They came to terrify the people, to rob them of their cattle, and to destroy their homes.

"They're at Crockett's farm!" Andy cried, bursting into the kitchen with Rob just behind him. "We saw them when we were coming home from Dan Hart's blacksmith shop. They've set fire to Mr. Crockett's barns, and they're stealing his horses and cows and—"

"And there's a British lieutenant going around to every house in the settlement," Rob broke in excitedly. "He's telling folks that Tarleton's on his way here with his troops. And we'll all be killed unless we'll take an oath and swear allegiance to the King."

"I'll *never* take such an oath," Andy cried angrily. He reached for the musket which hung over the fireplace. "I'll shoot that lieutenant before he ever gets up to this door."

"You'll do nothing of the kind!" his mother

[*49*]

said quickly. "We'll none of us take the oath. But we'll not stay here to be murdered, either. Round up the cattle, Andy. And head for North Carolina with them as fast as you can. Rob and I will pack up some things and—go on, Andy, hurry!"

Andy shook his head. "I'm not going till you promise me something," he announced stubbornly. "I'm thirteen, Mother. I can shoot as good as any man in the Waxhaws, and I want to fight the redcoats. Will you let me join our militia when we get to their camp?"

"If Andy joins, I'm going to join," Rob added quickly.

"All right," said Mrs. Jackson. "You're both too young to be soldiers. But these are dreadful times. Yes, you may join the militia if your Uncle Robert will let you. Now, hurry!"

Andy smiled. Without a word, he turned and raced for the pasture, whistling to Rover as he ran across the yard. Rob and his mother began to bundle up some food and clothing. And soon the Jacksons were hurrying along the road which led to North Carolina.

CHAPTER SIX

A Narrow Escape

ANDY JACKSON swung himself from his saddle and tied his horse to a hitching post near the steps of Uncle Robert's house. He spoke to Tige Wilson, who was standing guard at the door.

"Is Rob here?" he asked.

"He's inside, talking with Major Crawford," Tige replied, leaning on his musket. "Your Uncle James is there, too. Did Mart McGary track down Johnson and those other Tories who broke into his house when he was away?"

"Not yet," Andy said soberly. "He vows he'll catch them before the day's over, though. I wish those sneaking Tories would wear uniforms. Then we could spot them easy, like we do the redcoats."

"I sure wish *we* had uniforms," Tige declared. "I'd feel a lot more like a soldier if I had a blue coat with fancy trimmings, instead of this ragged shirt."

He stepped aside to let Andy pass. Pushing open the door, the boy went down the hall toward the big dining room, which Uncle Robert was using for an office. Nearly a year had passed since the Jacksons had fled to North Carolina, where Andy and Rob had joined the Waxhaws militia. They had all returned to the settlement with Major Crawford's troops.

After three hard-fought battles, the Americans had driven the British out of the back country. But Andy had not been allowed to take part in any of this fighting. Uncle Robert insisted that the boy was not yet old enough to be a real soldier.

"I need a mounted orderly," he had told Andy. "Someone who can ride like the wind and who knows all the paths and trails around here. You're just the fellow for that."

[*52*]

So Andy had carried important messages for Major Crawford to men in other parts of the back country. Now and then, he had also been allowed to do sentry duty.

He was hoping to be put on sentry duty again when he stepped into Major Crawford's dining room. But he forgot it at once when he saw the group gathered around the table.

Rob was there, looking as if he'd run five miles on a hot day. Uncle James and his married son, Tom, were standing near him. And all three were looking at a map which Uncle Robert had spread out before them.

Major Crawford glanced up at once when he heard Andy's step.

"Is your horse outside?" he asked.

"Yes, sir," Andy replied promptly.

"Then listen sharp," commanded Major Crawford. "Rob's just picked up some news over near Fishing Creek. The redcoats are coming back again, probably by this road." He pointed to a crooked line on the map. "We don't know how many there'll be or when they'll get here. But we'll need help in defending the settlement. Do you know where Captain Nesbit lives?"

"Yes, sir. I can get there in half an hour."

Major Crawford nodded. "Tell Nesbit to call together all the men he can, and to bring them to Waxhaws Church as soon as possible," he commanded. "We'll meet them there. That's all."

"Yes, sir," Andy said again. An instant later he was outside, unhitching his horse. Leaping into the saddle, he galloped up the road.

When he returned to the settlement an hour later, he found nearly forty men standing around the church yard. Their rifles were stacked near the door, and their horses were cropping grass close by. As Andy dismounted, Robert ran to meet him, and Major Crawford strode forward rapidly.

Andy saluted. "Captain Nesbit says he'll be on his way here as soon as he can get his men in from their fields," he announced breathlessly. "He said why in tarnation did this have to happen in the middle of corn-planting time, and—"

"Good work, Andy," interrupted Major Crawford. He turned on his heel and began talking with Tom Crawford in a low voice.

Andy tied his horse to a tree near Tom Crawford's brown mare. Then he splashed his hot face with water from the watering trough and dried it on the sleeve of his jacket. As he turned from the trough, his keen eyes spied a large group of men on horseback, a long way up the road.

"Hey! What's that?" he exclaimed.

"It's Nesbit's men!" Tige Wilson said.

A low murmur went through the waiting crowd.

"Captain Nesbit's coming! Praise God!"

"Here comes Nesbit with his men!"

Andy looked doubtful. "They must have ridden like chain lightning to get here so fast!" he exclaimed.

He jumped up on a stump to get a better view. Straining his eyes, he stared at the approaching horsemen. They were riding rapidly, four abreast, and half hidden by a cloud of dust.

"That's strange," Andy said to Rob, who had climbed up beside him. "Those men are coming from the right direction. But I can't make out Captain Nesbit at all. You'd think he'd be riding right in the first rank. I—"

He drew in his breath sharply. Suddenly the first ranks of horsemen had turned aside. And, charging forward, heading straight for the church, were redcoats! Scores of them! Spurring their horses! Waving their shining sabers in the April sun! And yelling as they came!

"Those were Tory skunks out in front!" Andy shouted, as a cry of dismay went up from Major Crawford's men. "They've tricked us! If I can lay my hands on a rifle, I'll—"

He leaped from the stump, with Robert

after him. In no time at all both boys were caught in a mass of struggling, shouting men and neighing, frightened horses.

Sabers flashed! Shots rang out! Bright red uniforms were everywhere!

Andy snatched up a rifle which had been dropped in the fighting. But a British soldier knocked it from his hands and sent him sprawling to the ground. As he scrambled to his feet, he saw flames and smoke rising from the roof of the church.

"They've set the church afire!" he yelled.

And then, above the din, Major Crawford's voice rang out strongly.

"Retreat!" cried Major Crawford. "We haven't a chance, men! Scatter in every direction. Then hide out, until—"

His words were choked off as two redcoats seized him and dragged him away. Quickly the Americans began to scatter. Leaping into their saddles, they rode off in every direction.

Andy and Tom Crawford galloped through the trees toward Cain Creek, with British riders thudding after them. Though the creek bottom was muddy, Andy's horse splashed across safely. But Tom Crawford's mare slipped and went down, throwing its rider into the shallow water.

Wheeling his horse around, Andy started back to help his cousin. Even as he did so, the first redcoat reached Tom and slashed at him with his saber.

"Keep going, Andy!" Tom shouted, struggling to his feet. "I'm caught. Don't let them get you! Here they come!"

And there were three more red-coated horsemen splashing into the creek.

There was nothing now that Andy could do to help Tom. Perhaps he could not even save himself. He slid from his saddle. Swiftly he knotted his reins so that they would not catch on anything.

"Go home," he said, giving his horse a slap. Then he ducked into the deep woods at the edge of the creek, and ran for all he was worth.

CHAPTER SEVEN

Andy Disobeys an Order

ANDY'S LEGS ached. For a long time he had been crouching in a clump of bushes while British soldiers searched the woods for him and for other Americans. Now it was nearly dark and he thought the redcoats had gone.

He stood up. Pushing his way quietly out of the bushes, he set off through the woods in the direction of Tom Crawford's house. Suddenly he stopped and his heart leaped to his mouth. In a thicket just ahead of him, someone had sneezed.

Then a familiar voice said, "Andy?" And Rob's tall figure rose from the thicket.

Andy gave a low whistle of relief. "Are you all right?" he asked as Rob came to meet him.

Rob nodded. "They caught Uncle James," he said.

"They caught Tom, too," Andy told him. "I'm going to his house now to tell his wife about it. Come on."

He started off again with Rob close behind him. But it was growing dark rapidly. Soon the boys could not tell which way they were going. There was no moon to light their way and at last they sat down under a huge oak to wait till morning.

They were cold and hungry and uneasy. With their backs against the big tree trunk, they talked in low tones about the attack at the church.

"Could you see who the Tories were who were riding out in front?" Rob asked.

"One of them was Johnson," Andy replied, hunching his knees up under his chin. "What do you think they'll do to Uncle Robert and Uncle James and Tom?"

"Throw them in prison somewhere and keep them till the war's over," Rob said.

Andy sighed impatiently and stared into the dark, longing to be on his way. As soon as it was light enough to see, he and Rob were on their feet and hurrying through the woods toward Tom's house.

The sun was up by the time they reached the place where the woods ended and Tom Crawford's clearing began. Rob looked warily around the clearing.

"I've got a feeling there's a Tory hiding behind every tree," he declared. "But I don't see a soul. Come on, let's run for it."

He and Andy ran across the clearing and burst into Tom Crawford's kitchen. They found Tom's wife sitting by the fire, feeding her baby. Andy started to tell her about her husband, but she interrupted him.

"I know what happened," she said. "John Thompson came over after dark last night to tell me. Have you boys been hiding in the woods all night?"

"Yes," Rob replied, "and we're starving."

"There's mush cooking in that pot over the fire," Mrs. Crawford said, laying little Tommy in his cradle. "Give it a stir, Andy, while I fetch some bowls."

Picking up a long wooden spoon, Andy did as he was told. In a few minutes he and Rob were seated at the table, eating hot mush and molasses.

Andy finished first and wiped his mouth on the back of his hand.

"Mother will be fretting about us," he said. "I'm going to light out for home."

Rob looked up quickly. "It's not safe yet, Andy," he declared. "The Tories—"

Suddenly he dropped his spoon and sprang to his feet. Someone was pounding on the door!

"Open!" a rough voice shouted. "Open up, you rebels, to the King's men!"

[63]

"Andy, hide!" Tom's wife whispered, snatching the baby from his cradle. "Rob, get upstairs! You—"

She gasped as the door was thrust open. Eight red-coated soldiers, carrying shining sabers, came crowding into the room. Behind them was an officer—a tall, scowling man with a cruel face. He looked about with a satisfied smile.

"Well, thanks to Johnson, we've caught two more traitors!" he exclaimed. "It's a good thing he saw these fellows run out of the woods. There may be other rebels hiding in this house, men. Search it!"

"With pleasure, Lieutenant," one of the redcoats replied. "Perhaps there's a traitor under here."

Pushing past Mrs. Crawford, he tipped over the table, and sent the dishes crashing to the floor. Another redcoat began to slash at the window curtains with his saber. And a third soldier yanked a little sheet from the baby's cradle. Andy snatched it from him.

"You stop that!" he cried angrily. "Let the things in this house alone, and—"

"Hold your tongue, you impudent young rebel!" the officer commanded sharply. "Take that rag you have in your hands and get down on your knees and clean off my boots."

Andy's eyes flashed. "I won't!" he cried, tossing the sheet back on the cradle. "You've made me a prisoner of war and I expect you to treat me like one."

The officer's face flamed with rage. "I command you to clean the mud off my boots!" he shouted, raising his sword.

"And I say I won't," Andy shouted back. "I—"

He flung up his arm to protect his face as the sword cut through the air. Mrs. Crawford screamed and Rob sprang to defend his brother. But blood was already spurting from a deep gash on Andy's hand, and streaming from a wide cut on his head.

"Now," cried the officer, turning angrily on Rob, "you clean my boots!"

"No!" Rob replied between clenched teeth. Then he winced as the sword fell again. Clapping his hand to his shoulder, he sank down on the bench near the fire.

[65]

By this time the baby was screaming with fright and Mrs. Crawford was sobbing.

"Coward," she cried, facing the British officer. "Trying to kill two unarmed boys. I—"

"Hush your noise," the officer said, putting his sword into its scabbard. "Put down that squalling child and bandage up that young traitor's head."

He motioned to Andy, who stood staring at his wounded hand, while blood ran slowly down his cheek.

Setting Tommy in his cradle, Mrs. Crawford took off her apron and quickly tore it into long wide strips. She wrapped one strip around Andy's head and then bandaged his hand up tightly.

The boy seemed dazed, but he refused to sit down. And he stood beside his brother until Mrs. Crawford had helped Rob take off his jacket and had bound up his wound.

"Are you all right, now, Rob?" Andy asked.

"I will be, in a minute," Rob said, breathing heavily. "What about you?"

"I'm—I'm fine!" Andy declared, holding

his bandaged head up proudly. "And some day—" He turned and looked steadily at the red-coated officer. "Some day," he said again, "I'll meet British soldiers in a *fair* fight."

"And then you won't forget what happened this morning, will you?" Rob asked weakly.

"I'll *never* forget," Andy replied firmly.

He glared at the officer. The officer glared back and shouted an order to his men, who were still smashing furniture and dishes. He commanded two of them to march Robert off to the British camp.

"Put him in with our other prisoners, and we'll take him to the jail in Camden," he said.

Then he turned to Andy.

"Now, my young gamecock," he exclaimed, "I'm going to give you a chance to serve your king! There's a rebel living near here named John Thompson. Lead us to his house, and don't try any tricks on us or we'll shoot you right through the head."

"No," Andy protested, pulling the bandage tighter on his hand. "I won't do it. Mr. Thompson's our friend. I—"

[*67*]

"Someday, I'll meet British soldiers in a fair fight."

He hesitated as the officer fingered the hilt of his sword. Just then Mrs. Crawford touched the boy's arm.

"Take them to the house, Andy," she begged. "Maybe Mr. Thompson won't be there. Maybe he'll have some men with him. Lead them there. You'll be killed if you don't."

"He will, indeed," one of the redcoats declared. And he shoved Andy out into the yard.

Five minutes later the boy was mounted on a horse, leading the British soldiers down the road. His head and hand throbbed with pain. He was worried about what would happen to Rob in the Camden jail. And he was afraid he would never see his brother or his mother again.

"I guess the British will shoot me all right," he thought forlornly, as he turned his horse up a narrow lane. "Because I'm going to trick them somehow and find a way to save John Thompson, if I can."

CHAPTER EIGHT

In a British Jail

THE British jail in Camden was filled with American prisoners. The room on the second story was crowded. Two of the prisoners were sick with smallpox.

Andy Jackson stepped over a man who lay on the floor, tossing and moaning. He sat down against the wall beside Dan Hart, the Waxhaws blacksmith. Then he unwound the blood-stained bandage which was wrapped around his hand. He and Dan examined the cut.

"That's healing up real good!" Dan declared. "How's your head?"

"Better," Andy replied, binding up his hand again. "I wish I knew about Rob, though. His shoulder was slashed clear to the bone, Dan. And they shoved him into that room downstairs so hard that he—"

Dan interrupted him. "Rob will be all right!" he exclaimed, trying to sound cheerful. "But it was a mean trick to separate you."

He leaned across Andy and spoke to a graybearded man who sat near by. "Hey, Jack," he said, "this is the fellow I told you about. The boy who fooled the British last week when they went to capture John Thompson. Tell him how you did it, Andy."

"It was easy, once I had figured it out," Andy said, hunching his knees up under his chin. "I knew if we went to Mr. Thompson's house by the regular road he couldn't see us coming.

"So I led the redcoats across a big field, and Mr. Thompson spotted us while we were half a mile away. He jumped on his horse and got across the creek. And the British were mad as hornets."

Dan Hart chuckled. "It makes me laugh every time I think about it," he said. "It's lucky

[71]

for you, though, that the lieutenant found out you were only fourteen and decided not to shoot you."

He looked up at the sound of keys rattling outside the door. The jailer entered the room, bringing several loaves of stale bread and a small kettle of soup. This was the prisoners' only meal for the day.

Andy ate his share greedily. He was almost as hungry when he had finished as when he had begun. Tightening his belt, he walked over to the barred window at one end of the room.

A strong stockade surrounded the prison yard. The British camp lay just beyond it, and soldiers in scarlet coats were drilling in the bright April sunshine. Andy watched them for a while. Then, with a sigh, he turned away.

His wounds were still painful and he was weak from hunger. The Tory jailer had stolen his shoes and jacket. Though the day was warm, he shivered as he sat down again beside Dan.

There was nothing to do in the prison and

the days dragged by slowly. Before the week was out, one of the men who had smallpox was dead. And several more prisoners had come down with the dreadful disease.

"We'll all of us get it if we have to stay here much longer," Dan Hart said gloomily to Andy one evening.

They were standing at the window when he spoke, looking out at the British camp and the country beyond it. Suddenly Andy's sharp eyes caught sight of men moving about on a hill some distance away. He peered at them sharply and then whooped with joy.

"Look!" he cried excitedly. "Americans! Over there on the hill. They're—"

The rest of his sentence was lost as every prisoner who was able to walk came crowding around the window. And what they saw set them all to cheering. For a large army of Americans was making camp on Hobkirk's Hill.

The prisoners felt sure now that they would soon be rescued. That night they talked hopefully about what they would do when the

Americans opened the jail and set them free. All the next day they waited anxiously for a battle to begin.

For five days they waited, but nothing happened. Then on the evening of the fifth day, three British soldiers came into the room,

bringing a carpenter with them. They ordered the prisoners roughly away from the window and the carpenter began to board it up.

Some of the prisoners protested angrily at this but the soldiers silenced them quickly.

"We've just found out that those rebels on
the hill haven't any cannon," the tallest red-

coat announced. "So we're going to surprise
them tomorrow and cut them to mincemeat.

You wouldn't want to see that happen, would you?"

"They'll cut *you* into mincemeat," Andy muttered, clenching his fists. "They'll—"

He shut his lips firmly when the redcoat moved toward him. And he did not speak again until the soldiers and the carpenter had left the room. Then he stepped quickly to the window.

"If there's going to be a battle tomorrow, we're going to see it," he declared, running his hand over one of the boards. "I'll fool those old buzzards. Someone give me that razor we use for cutting up our bread, and I'll cut a peephole in this middle plank."

One of the prisoners handed Andy an old dull razor and the boy went to work.

Next morning when the fighting began, Andy Jackson was watching it. For hours he stood with his eye glued to the peephole, describing the battle to the other prisoners. At first all went well with the American soldiers. They met the surprise attack bravely and sent the redcoats running helter-skelter. But the

English soldiers advanced again and drove the Americans from the hill.

When the battle was over, Andy turned from the peephole and sat down in the corner with his face buried in his hands. All hope of freedom seemed gone. Never before had he been so discouraged or unhappy. To make matters worse, he was beginning to feel very sick, and before the day ended he knew that he had caught the smallpox.

The next morning he lay on the floor, weak with fever. Suddenly the door opened and the jailer stuck his head inside the room.

"Jackson!" he shouted. "Andrew Jackson! You're wanted below!"

Andy looked at Dan in dismay. "What's anyone want *me* for?" he asked. "Do you think they're going to flog me, Dan, for making that peephole?"

"Jackson!" the jailer shouted before Dan could answer. "Come along. I can't wait here all day."

Andy stumbled to his feet. With his heart pounding, he followed the jailer down the

[77]

stairs to the door of the prison. Then he stopped and stared as though he could not believe his eyes. For Rob sat slumped on the prison steps, and his mother stood beside him.

"Andy," cried Mrs. Jackson softly, as she put her arms around her youngest son. "Oh, Andy." Then she stepped back and peered up into his face.

"Lord save us, lad! You've got smallpox, too. Poor boy! You do look dreadful. But you're not near as sick with it as Rob is. He doesn't even know me, Andy. We must get him home as soon as ever we can."

Andy leaned against the door to steady himself. "Home?" he asked, in a puzzled voice.

"Yes," his mother said quickly. "I've arranged it with the British commander. He's letting you boys go free in exchange for two redcoats that our Waxhaws men captured. I've a couple of horses outside the stockade, Andy. If we can get Rob on one—"

"Of course we can," Andy declared stoutly. His head was spinning. His legs would hardly hold him up. But he suddenly felt stronger than he had felt for many days.

"Come on, Rob," he said.

Putting his arm around his brother, he hoisted Rob to his feet. With the older boy leaning on him heavily, he started across the prison yard. And within a few minutes the Jacksons had begun their weary journey home.

It was many hours later when they reached the Waxhaws. A heavy rain was falling, and all three were soaked to the skin. Rob was delirious with fever. As for poor Andy, he had just enough strength left to stagger into the house and fall onto a bed.

For weeks he was so ill that he did not know what was going on around him. And when he grew better he heard dreadful news. His dear brother, Rob, had died two days after they had reached home.

One hot August morning, Andy sat propped against his pillows, thinking about Rob as he waited for his breakfast. When his mother bustled into the room with a tray in her hands, Andy looked at her in surprise.

"Why are you wearing your bonnet?" he asked. "Where are you going?"

"To Charleston," Mrs. Jackson replied, setting the tray on a table near Andy's bed. "Bill and Joe Crawford are prisoners there in the British jail, and they're sick with a terrible fever. They've no one to nurse them. But you're strong enough now so that I can leave you, and—"

"Will you be gone long?" Andy asked unhappily.

"I don't know," said his mother. "Tom Crawford's wife will be here to take care of you, and if anything should happen—"

She stopped speaking suddenly and tried to smile. "You're a good boy, Andy," she went on. "But there are some things I want you to remember always, whether I'm here or not.

"Never tell a lie. Fight hard for things you know are right. And stick to your friends through thick and thin. A body needs friends in this world. Will you remember that?"

"Yes," Andy promised soberly. "I will. You take good care of yourself in that Charleston jail, Mother. And—and come back safely."

His mother nodded and stooped to kiss his forehead. Then, wiping her eyes on her apron, she hurried from the room.

Andrew Jackson never saw his mother again. On a cold, gray day in November he learned that she was dead.

"She caught the fever in the prison, Andy," Mrs. Crawford told him, with tears running down her cheeks. "And she was all worn out with nursing. She just couldn't get well. Look, here's her clothes they've sent you."

She handed Andy a little bundle. The boy stared at it blindly. How could his mother be dead? It was impossible to believe.

"But I must believe it," he told himself

[*81*]

sternly. "I'll never see her again. Never. I'll never hear her laugh. I'll—"

Suddenly Andy buried his face in the bundle and his body shook with sobs. He felt completely alone in the world.

CHAPTER NINE

Andy Makes a Great Decision

IT WAS a sunny afternoon in March nearly two years later. The Revolutionary War was over. The British had been defeated. The United States were independent at last. And peace had come to the Waxhaws.

Major Robert Crawford sat on his low porch steps talking to his brother, James. The two men were discussing young Andrew Jackson.

"Maybe I made a mistake when I asked Andy to live here," Major Crawford said, setting his old cocked hat down beside him. "I thought the boy would be better off with me than with you, after his mother died. But he's as wild and hot-headed as ever."

Uncle James mopped his forehead with a

bright red handkerchief and started to speak. But Major Crawford went on quickly.

"I sent him back to school and he wouldn't study!" he exclaimed impatiently. "I apprenticed him to Joe White to learn saddle making and he quit after six months because he didn't like it. Now he spends his days hunting and tearing around the country on his horse, or going to cockfights."

Uncle James shook his head. "It's high time he settled down to something," he remarked. "He was sixteen last week. Look! Here he comes now, riding like an Indian on the warpath."

And there was Andy, galloping up the road with his red hair flying in the breeze. He pulled his horse up sharply when he reached the house. Leaping from his saddle, he thrust a sheet of paper at his uncles.

"The post-rider just stopped me on the road," he cried, "and gave me this! It's a letter! For me! Read it!"

His bright blue eyes danced as he stood beside his horse, waiting impatiently for his un-

Leaping from his saddle, he thrust a piece of paper at his uncles

cles to read the letter. Uncle James finished
first.

"This *is* good news!" he exclaimed with a
smile. "I'd forgotten you had a grandfather in
Ireland, Andy."

"So had I," Andy replied, grinning broadly.
"My mother used to tell us about him when
we were little. But I haven't thought of him
for years and now—"

"Now he's died and left you fifteen hundred
dollars!" Major Crawford broke in. "That's a
tidy sum, my boy. What do you plan to do with
it?"

Andy laughed. "I haven't had time to think
about that, sir," he replied. "I'll have to collect
the money in Charleston. That's what the letter says. I'll pack my saddlebags now and leave
early tomorrow morning."

He reached for the letter and put it into his
pocket. Feeling grown-up and very independent, he led his horse to the stable and went in-
doors to prepare for his journey.

Since the death of his mother, Andy had
been restless and lonely. Though his uncles

were kind, they were both busy with their own affairs. And the boy had often felt that no one really cared what happened to him. Now, thanks to a grandfather he had never seen, he had enough money to get a good start in life.

"And I won't waste a penny of it," he told himself, as he stuffed his saddlebags with shirts and stockings. "Not a penny."

Early the next morning he said good-by to his uncles and set off for Charleston, one hundred and fifty miles away.

It was a fine spring day. Peach trees and dogwood bloomed pink and white on the hillsides. Cardinals flashed their scarlet wings as they flitted from tree to tree. The sky was blue. The sun was warm. And Andy whistled happily as he rode away from the Waxhaws.

He was not whistling when he rode home many weeks later. His thoughts were sober and his pockets were empty.

"Do you mean to tell me that you have *no* money left?" Uncle Robert asked sharply, as they sat at the supper table on the night Andy reached home.

Andy's face flushed. "That's right, sir," he replied, looking straight at his uncle. "My fifteen hundred dollars is gone."

"But what did you do with it?" Uncle Robert demanded.

"Spent it," said Andy. "I didn't intend to, of course. But there was so much to do in Charleston, and so much to see. They have a fine race track there, sir. I went every day and—"

"And you bet on the horses?" Uncle Robert broke in.

"Yes, sir."

"So all you have to show for your fifteen hundred dollars are some ruffled shirts and fancy knee breeches!" Uncle Robert exclaimed in disgust.

Andy nodded. "It was foolish," he admitted, "but I've learned a lesson."

"A pretty expensive one!" Uncle Robert declared hotly. He slapped the table. "I tell you, Andrew, you can't go on this way. Idle! Wasteful! Good for nothing! What do you intend to do with yourself, now that you've come back without a penny? I suppose you haven't given it a thought."

"But I have," Andy said quickly. "I've been thinking about it most of the way home. It's time I made my own way in the world. I'm going to study hard for a few months longer and then I think I'll be a schoolmaster."

Uncle Robert looked doubtful. "Well, that might be worth trying," he said.

The very next day Andy went to work at his studies. Before long he was able to get a teaching job in the Waxhaws.

The children liked their tall young schoolmaster, with his quick smile and snapping

[*89*]

blue eyes. And Andy liked his pupils. But he soon grew tired of hearing them recite their ABC's and of correcting their sums. He also grew tired of hearing his uncles remind him of how he had wasted his money in Charleston.

One snowy afternoon George McWhorter stopped in at the school just as Andy was setting out for home. As the two friends walked down the road Andy suddenly announced that he was going to leave the Waxhaws.

"I've decided to go to Salisbury to study law with a man named Spruce Macay," he said. "Then, as soon as I get to be a lawyer, I'm going to head over the mountains for Nashville, in the Western District."

"The Western District!" George exclaimed. "Isn't that Indian country?"

"Some Indians still think it is," Andy said. "And they make plenty of trouble there, too. But there are hundreds of settlers living in the District already. And more people are moving out there all the time. I believe that in a few years a lawyer could make a fortune there."

"Maybe," George said doubtfully. "What do your uncles think about it?"

Andy shrugged his shoulders. "Oh, they'll be glad to get rid of me," he said, with a grin. "Uncle Robert told me last night that I'd come to a bad end as sure as a cat has kittens."

George smiled and looked at his friend thoughtfully. Suddenly a picture flashed through his mind. A picture of two boys fighting on a hot summer day and rolling in the dust.

"You won't come to a bad end!" he exclaimed, clapping Andy on the back. "You'll do something big some day, you red-headed rooster—because you won't stay throwed."

He raised his elbow when Andy laughed and lunged at him. For a minute the two young men pushed each other about. Then Andy broke away suddenly and leaped over the fence.

"Good-by," he shouted over his shoulder. And he strode across the snowy field toward Uncle Robert's house.

Three days later, with his saddlebags bulging and his rifle slung over his shoulder, Andy Jackson rode into the town of Salisbury, North Carolina. He had left the Waxhaws forever.

CHAPTER TEN

By Wagon Train to Nashville

THE road that led to Nashville, in the Western District, was rough and narrow. The long wagon train moved slowly. It was growing dark and the travelers were tired.

For two days and a night they had been passing through country where unfriendly Indians often attacked white people. The leader of the wagon train had refused to let the travelers stop anywhere for more than an hour. They were glad now when he turned his horse and shouted, "We're safe here. All wagons, halt for the night."

Slowly the white-topped wagons rolled to a stop in a large open space among the trees. Old Granny Wilson, who had been dozing in the last wagon, woke with a start.

"What's the matter, Mary?" she asked the young woman who sat on the wagon seat. "Why are we stopping?"

"Because we're going to camp here all night," replied her granddaughter. "We're safe from Indians here and we can get a real good sleep. Look, Granny! Mr. Jackson and his friends have started some fires already."

"Jackson?" quavered Granny Wilson. "Who's he?"

"Oh, he's that tall thin fellow from Salisbury," Mary Wilson replied. "The one with the scar on his forehead. Come. Jed wants to help us down."

She stretched out her hand to her brother, who had come to help her. All about her, women and children were climbing wearily from other wagons. And men were beginning to unharness or unsaddle their horses.

Several fires were already burning brightly, and it did not take the travelers long to make camp and cook supper. By the time the first stars were out, the women and children were asleep in little shelters of boughs and buffalo

[*93*]

skins. The men and older boys lay rolled in blankets near the fires. All except Andrew Jackson and his friend, Tom Searcy.

Those young men were not sleepy. They sat together under a tree at the edge of the camp, smoking their corncob pipes and talking in low tones. At last Tom Searcy got up.

"Yes, I reckon George Washington would be a mighty good man for our first president," he said drowsily. "Well, I'm going to roll in. You better get to bed, too, Andy. We'll be on the road by daybreak."

"I'll be along soon," Andy replied.

He watched Tom roll up in a blanket near one of the fires. Then he leaned back against the tree, with his rifle beside him. He wondered why he didn't feel like sleeping, why he found himself listening, listening.

It was a warm silent night. Bright stars winked above him, and the big September moon hung over the black trees. Suddenly, from the deep forest came a soft little cry that made Andy jump. Then he grinned.

"Just some owls hooting," he said to himself, as he leaned back against his tree. He puffed contentedly on his pipe, thinking of many things. He was having a good time on this journey to Nashville. Indeed, he had been having a good time ever since he had left the Waxhaws. Too good a time, perhaps.

He knew well how most of the people in Salisbury felt about him. Only the day before he had left there he had heard one man tell another that Andrew Jackson was the most roaring, frolicking, game-cocking, horse-racing, mischievous fellow who had ever lived in the town.

"But I learned to be a lawyer, anyhow," Andy told himself with satisfaction. "And when I get to Nashville, folks will find out that I'm a good one, too."

He knocked the ashes from his pipe. Settling himself more comfortably against the tree, he closed his eyes.

"Hoot! Hoot! Hoot!" The owl calls were closer now. From the woods on the other side of the camp came a long, low "Whoo-oo-oo."

"That's strange," thought Andy, yawning.

[95]

"Never heard owls make such a racket. Sounds like they were talking to each other."

Talking! In an instant Andy was wide awake and listening intently. Suddenly he grabbed his rifle. Crawling over to Tom Searcy, he shook him roughly.

"Tom!" he whispered. "That hooting! Do you hear it? Those aren't owls making that noise, Tom. They're Indians! Signaling to each other! They're all around us!"

"Couldn't be," Tom muttered. "We haven't seen a redskin since we left—"

"Listen!" urged Andy.

Raising himself on his elbow, Tom listened for several minutes. "Maybe you're right," he said, getting to his feet. "What will we do?"

"Wake everybody up, and get them on the road before we're attacked," Andy replied quickly. "We mustn't make any noise about it, either."

He crawled over to the men who were sleeping around the fire and began to wake them. Warning them to keep quiet, he went on to wake others.

Soon all the travelers were stirring. Frightened women gathered their children together and scurried for the wagons. Men harnessed or saddled their horses as quietly as possible. Then, slowly and silently the wagon train moved off down the shadowy road.

Not until noon the next day did the travelers stop to rest. They were exhausted. And half the men in the party were complaining about Andrew Jackson.

"Crazy young fool!" grumbled black-bearded David McBride as he watered his horses. "He don't know a hoot owl from an Indian. I'll bet my bottom dollar there wasn't a redskin within fifty miles of that camping place."

"He's crazy, all right," agreed Jed Wilson. "Why, my old granny was so scared she's still shaking, all because of Jackson. Just wait till I—hey, who's that coming up the road?"

He pointed to a rider who was galloping toward them. When the man reached the wagons, he pulled up his horse and slid from his saddle. The travelers gathered around him quickly.

The stranger's face was white. His shirt was stained with blood. One arm hung useless by his side.

"Indians!" he gasped. "They killed everyone—but me. We'd been hunting all day—five of us—and we found some fires burning, so we—"

"Where?" demanded Tom Searcy. "Where were the fires?"

"A long way back—where a lot of folks had been camping," the man answered. "But—they'd gone, so we lay down to sleep. And just —as it was getting light—the Indians came tearing out of the woods and—"

The stranger groaned and slumped to the ground. Tom and Andy and David McBride picked him up gently and put him into one of the wagons, where two of the women bandaged his wounds. Then the travelers set out again, for they were eager to get as far as possible from the Indians.

No one in that wagon train called Andrew Jackson crazy now. The women said he had saved their lives and began to talk about what good manners he had and how kind he was to all the children.

The men admired him because he had thought and acted so quickly. And two nights later, when Andy shot a panther which had attacked one of the horses, everyone praised him to the skies.

For nearly a month the wagon train journeyed on through the wilderness. Then, one day late in October, the travelers reached the crest of a hill and below them lay Nashville.

"It doesn't look like much," Tom Searcy declared, staring at the cluster of log houses, bark tents, and wagon camps.

Andy laughed. "It'll grow," he remarked.

"Come on, Tom, I'll race you into town."

He spoke to his horse and galloped down
the winding road, with Tom pounding behind him. That night the two friends stayed at
the Red Heifer Tavern on the settlement's
main street. But it was noisy and dirty and the
food was poor. So Andy went to board with

the Widow Donelson in her comfortable log house, nearly ten miles from town.

There he met Mrs. Donelson's youngest daughter, Rachel. Andrew Jackson soon fell in love with this beautiful, dark-haired girl. After a time, Rachel knew that she loved him, too. And on an August day nearly three years after the wagon train reached Nashville, Andrew and Rachel were married.

By this time, young Lawyer Jackson was well known in the Western District. As he had traveled from one little court to another he had met many settlers and made many friends. He had begun to make money, too. Men often paid him for his law work with large tracts of land. And he was able to sell many acres of this land to new settlers at good prices.

In Nashville people told Mrs. Jackson that they thought her husband was becoming one of the most important men in the town. But they never dreamed, as they said this, that he would some day be one of the greatest men in the whole United States.

CHAPTER ELEVEN

"We'll Teach Them a Lesson!"

IT WAS early in the evening of a warm spring day. In their beautiful home called Hunter's Hill the Jacksons were having a party. Several friends were there. And so were all of Rachel Jackson's ten brothers and sisters with their wives or husbands and their children.

Chairs had been pushed back against the walls of the big drawing room. A Negro fiddler was playing a rollicking tune, and nearly everyone was dancing.

Andrew Jackson swung his plump little partner around and around again, so fast that her feet left the floor. When the music stopped he set her down with a chuckle.

"Are you dizzy?" he asked.

Mrs. Jackson laughed and caught at his arm to steady herself.

"Of course I'm dizzy," she panted. "But I'm so happy to have you home again that I could dance all night. Mercy me! Look at those naughty boys. I'll have to go and stop them."

Quickly she crossed to the other end of the room. Two of her little nephews were rolling on the floor fighting over a piece of sugar candy. She separated the boys and gave half the candy to Jack and the rest to his younger brother, John. Then she started back to join her husband. But the fiddler had begun to play "Possum up a Gum Tree." And Andrew Jackson was already whirling and jigging with another partner.

Mrs. Jackson fanned herself with her handkerchief and watched him for a moment. How tall and handsome he looked in his black suit and fine ruffled shirt! She was very proud of him. And she was proud of all that he had accomplished since they had been married.

In 1796, five years after their marriage, the

Western District had become one of the United States. Andrew Jackson had helped draw up a government for this new state, which was the sixteenth state to join the Union. He had also suggested an Indian name for it—Tennessee.

Then the people of Tennessee had elected him as their first Representative to Congress. Next they had made him a Senator. Now he was the Major General of the Tennessee militia and a judge in the state's Supreme Court.

He was a good judge, too—one of the best in Tennessee. The roughest rascals in the state had learned that he was afraid of no one. Though he was sometimes hot-tempered, he was always fair and quick to punish those who had done wrong.

Of course, when court was in session, Judge Jackson was often away from home. When he returned from these trips, Mrs. Jackson sometimes invited friends and relatives to Hunter's Hill for a celebration.

Now she turned as a servant appeared at the

door to say that supper was ready. The fiddler finished his tune and the dancing stopped. Andrew Jackson caught up the little Donelson boys, one under each arm, and led the way into the dining room.

Everyone trooped after him, laughing and talking, and found seats at the long table. Chicken pot pies, roasts of beef, hot biscuits, golden honey, spiced fruits and juicy strawberry tarts disappeared in no time.

Then the children went out to play on the wide lawn in the light of the setting sun. And the grownups gathered around Mrs. Jackson's harpsichord to sing, while Andrew Jackson played the flute.

It was late when the party ended and the Jacksons were left alone. They stood together on the low veranda, watching the last guest ride away.

Stars blinked overhead and the night air was fragrant with the smell of honeysuckle and roses. Andrew Jackson sat down on the step and pulled his wife down beside him.

For a time they discussed the party. Then Andrew Jackson said slowly, "Rachel, I've something unpleasant to tell you, and I might as well tell it right now. I've decided today that I must resign as a judge."

"Why?" asked Mrs. Jackson in surprise.

"Because I'm away so much of the time looking after other people's business that I can't look after our own affairs properly," her husband replied. "I've let things get into a mess, Rachel; I'm in debt up to my ears and I hate to owe money. I want to sell Hunter's Hill, pay my debts and start all over again. Would you mind?"

"Not a bit," Mrs. Jackson declared. "We can move into the old blockhouse on the Hermitage land you bought a few years ago. And I'll like it because I'll have you at home all the time."

Andrew Jackson smiled. "You're the most wonderful wife any man ever had," he said gratefully. "You deserve the very best of everything and I mean to see that you get it."

He patted her hand, glad to have the matter settled. Within a short time he had resigned as a judge. He had sold his big plantation. And the Jacksons had moved into the old Hermitage blockhouse, two miles away.

Carpenters had already cut windows in the thick log walls and built a separate cabin for a kitchen as well as another for guests. Mrs. Jackson bustled about, helping servants hang curtains and arrange furniture. Soon the house was settled and homelike.

Relatives and friends visited the Hermitage

often. And the little Donelson boys thought it was one of the nicest places in the world. When their father died that winter and their mother could not take care of them, John and Jack went to the Hermitage to live.

Meanwhile, Andrew Jackson was very busy. He had planted many acres of cotton on the Hermitage land. Now he put men to work building keel-boats to carry the cotton to market in New Orleans. He opened a store at Clover Bottom, three miles away, and he built a race course near-by.

John and Jack liked to go with him when he went to the stables at Clover Bottom where he kept his race horses. One of these animals—a beautiful stallion named Truxton—was the most famous horse in Tennessee.

Truxton won many races and Andrew Jackson made a great deal of money on the horse. He was doing well in business, too. Before long he was able to improve his plantation. He bought a handsome carriage for his wife. And he sent the Donelson boys to a good private school.

[*109*]

Since the school was in Nashville, eight miles away, the boys boarded there. But they often went home for short visits. One winter day when they arrived at the Hermitage they found their Aunt Rachel sitting before the fire with a tiny baby in her arms.

"He's going to be our very own," Mrs. Jackson said, looking down proudly at the baby. "My brother Severn's wife had twins, and she's given us this one to keep forever. We've adopted him and his name is Andrew Jackson, junior. Don't you think he's beautiful?"

John peered into the baby's little red face and said "yes," politely. But ten-year-old Jack just shrugged his shoulders.

"Babies cry all the time," he declared. "Where's Uncle Andrew?"

"At a meeting of the militia," Mrs. Jackson replied. "He won't be home until supper time."

Jack made a wry face and went to hang up his coat. It seemed to him that his uncle was always at militia meetings these days. And indeed, Major General Jackson was spending much of his time drilling men or reading books about making war. For trouble had arisen again between the English and the Americans.

It had started because England was fighting a war with France and needed men desperately for her navy. Captains of powerful English vessels were stopping American ships at sea and kidnapping sailors from them. England was also trying to prevent American ships from landing at French ports.

"And they'd better let us and our ships alone!" Andrew Jackson said hotly at supper that night. "Or, by the Eternal, we'll teach them a lesson they'll never forget."

He pounded the table so hard that his plate jumped and gravy splattered over his gold-trimmed uniform.

John leaned forward eagerly, his eyes shining with excitement.

"Do you mean you think we'll really have another war with England?" he asked.

"I do," his uncle replied grimly. "And

[*111*]

when that war comes, your uncle Andrew and the Tennessee militia will be ready to fight until the British are licked to a frazzle."

The war which Andrew Jackson expected broke out on June 18th, 1812. General Jackson offered his services at once to his country. But for one reason or another, many months passed before he was given a chance to fight. Then it was not against the British that he led the Tennessee militia. It was against a nearer and more crafty enemy—Indians.

CHAPTER TWELVE

Old Hickory

Rachel Jackson hurried up the stairs and into the sunlit bedroom on the second floor of the Hermitage. She spoke to her husband, who lay in bed with his left arm and shoulder swathed in bandages.

"Governor Blount and his friend have gone," she told him. "They just rode off through the gate. Why did they come here to see you, Andrew? What's wrong?"

"Indians!" Andrew Jackson said shortly. "Chief Red Eagle has started a thousand Creeks on the warpath. They've killed more than two hundred and fifty settlers down at Fort Mims and—"

[*113*]

"Fort Mims?" Mrs. Jackson broke in anxiously. "Where's that?"

"Down south in the Mississippi Territory," her husband replied. "The British have been trying to stir up the Indians north of here since the war started. But no one expected trouble from the Creeks."

He raised himself higher against his pillows and winced as he moved his bandaged arm.

"Please fetch me a pen and some paper," he went on. "I must send out orders to my officers at once. I've told Governor Blount that we'll be ready to leave for Creek country in nine days."

"Leave!" Mrs. Jackson looked at him in amazement.

Two weeks earlier, in a bitter quarrel, he had been shot twice by a man named Jesse Benton. He had nearly died of his wounds.

"You're still too weak to walk!" Mrs. Jackson protested.

"I'll be walking nine days from now, all right," her husband declared. "Those red devils must be wiped out, Rachel, or no settler in the Mississippi Territory will be safe. And you mustn't fret about me, my dear. I feel stronger already. Will you fetch me my writing materials now?"

"Yes," Mrs. Jackson said unhappily. And she hurried away to get him what he needed.

Soon Andrew Jackson was writing out orders for his officers, listing the supplies he must have for his men, and planning a war against the Creeks. Nine days later, with his arm in a sling, he stood on the Hermitage steps saying good-by to his family.

"Watch over your aunt till I get back," he told the Donelson boys. Then he kissed his wife and little Andrew. One of the Negro servants helped him mount his horse. And off he rode to meet his troops, who were waiting for him in Fayetteville, eighty miles to the south. Before long he was leading them further south, deep into Red Eagle's country.

There were twenty-five hundred men in Jackson's army, on foot and on horseback. Officers in bright red jackets and soiled white pantaloons. Soldiers in dark blue homespun coats and trousers. Hunters and scouts in leather breeches and deerskin shirts. And a hundred or more Indians—for the Choctaws and Cherokees were friendly to the white men, and so were many of the Creeks.

Day after day the army pushed on through the wilderness. At last the men reached the Coosa River, where some of them made camp, and others began to build a fort. It was the first day of November. The air was crisp and cool. The men were in good spirits. They laughed and joked as they sat around their fires that night. But they talked soberly when they spoke of the families they had left behind them and the fighting which was ahead.

At one fire a scout named Davy Crockett was cleaning his rifle.

"Got to have her slick as a whistle tomor-

row," he said to the men who were with him. "There's two hundred Red Sticks holed up in some place called Tallushatchee and we're going there with Colonel Coffee to cook them up to cracklin'."

"Coffee's a good man," drawled tall Tim Colbert. "But I sure wish the General was well enough to lead us. I'd follow Old Hickory anywhere."

"Why do you call him 'Old Hickory'?" Davy asked.

Tim laughed. "I reckon you ain't been with this army long!" he exclaimed. "A lot of us fellows gave the General that name more than a year ago.

"It was all on account of some mix-up in the War Department in Washington. First they wanted us to go to New Orleans in case the British made an attack there. Then, when we'd got clear to Natchez, they changed their minds. Sent word to the General that we weren't needed and ordered him to dismiss us right away and—"

"And they hadn't even paid us!" young Bill

Smithers interrupted indignantly. "We didn't have any supplies. Some of our men were too sick to walk. And the General was mad as hops. He swore he wouldn't dismiss us till he got us back to Tennessee, no matter what the War Department ordered, so—"

He coughed as the wind shifted and blew smoke in his face. Tim went on with the story.

"So he hired wagons for the fellows who was sick, with his own money, he did, and bought food and marched us home," Tim said. "Eight hundred miles it was, too, through country 'most as wild as this. But he gave his horse to young Pete Holston, 'cause Pete had hurt his leg, and *he* walked the whole way, right along with the rest of us."

"Never seemed to get tired, either," Bill added. "And he was always cheerful. We got to saying he was tough as old hickory, and pretty soon that's what we were calling him— Old Hickory. And he don't mind it a bit."

"He'll mind it if we don't lick those Creeks tomorrow," Tim declared. "I'm going to turn in and get some rest."

He lay down and covered himself in a blanket. The others soon followed his example. Before long the entire camp was quiet.

The next day Colonel Coffee and his men rode off to attack Tallushatchee. From the opening in his tent, General Jackson watched them leave. He longed to be leading them. But he was still too weak to be of much use in a fight. Also he had important work to do in camp.

The wagon loads of food which should have been sent to him had not arrived. Game was scarce in the surrounding country. Now many of the men were beginning to complain of hunger.

"We'll have a famine here if we don't get supplies soon," he thought. And, turning on his heel, he sat down at his table and picked up his long quill pen. All day he was busy, writing letters and sending out messengers. He asked help of everyone who might send on provisions for his hungry army.

The next day he inspected Fort Strother, which was almost finished, and waited eagerly for Colonel Coffee's troops to return. It was nightfall before they came riding back to camp. They had good news. After a savage battle they had killed all the Creek warriors who had gathered at Tallushatchee. They had also brought back a number of Creek women and children as captives.

"Poor creatures, they're a sad-looking lot!" General Jackson exclaimed as he and Colonel Coffee inspected the prisoners. "See that they're properly cared for, John."

He stopped beside a little black-haired boy who stood alone, crying bitterly. "What's the matter with this child?" he asked. "Where's his mother?"

"She was killed in the fighting," replied Colonel Coffee. "The other squaws won't take care of him, and I don't know what's going to become of him."

Jackson looked down thoughtfully at the boy. "He's about the same age as my Andrew," he remarked. "I wonder—" Suddenly he smiled. "I'll look after him," he added.

Taking the weeping child by the hand, he

[*121*]

led him into his tent, where he mixed together some brown sugar and water. Then he lifted the little Indian boy to his knee and coaxed him to drink it.

"Lincoyer," he said gently. "That's what we'll call you—Lincoyer. And tomorrow I'll send you home to Rachel to be a brother to Andrew. Here, drink a little more."

The child stared at him with wide eyes. He could not understand a word this strange white man said. But the man's voice was kind. His arm was strong and steady. And the brown sugar mixture was good. Slowly Lincoyer's sobs died away and he fell asleep against the General's shoulder.

Early the next morning a rider left camp, taking Lincoyer to join his new family. Hardly had they gone when Andrew Jackson was hard at work again, writing for supplies and planning the next move against Red Eagle and his warriors. But before he could make that move, a surprising thing happened.

It was nearly dusk two days later when a

Creek Indian raced into camp. In his hair he wore a white deer's tail, which was a sign that he was friendly to the white men. He was breathless and almost too tired to speak. But he gasped out his story as best he could. And a strange story it was.

A hundred and fifty-four Creeks, who had refused to join Red Eagle in his fight against the white men, were cooped up in a small fort at Talledaga, thirty miles away. For several days they had been surrounded by a thousand of Red Eagle's braves.

"No food!" gasped the man with the deer's tail in his hair. "No water! Send help or all die."

"How did you get out past Red Eagle's men?" General Jackson asked sharply.

"Put skin over me," the Indian replied. "Hog skin. When night come I do like this."

He dropped to all fours and began to creep quietly around the tent.

"Can you get back into the fort?" the General asked as the Creek stood up.

[*123*]

The Indian nodded.

"Then go and tell your friends we're coming to help them," Jackson commanded.

The Indian disappeared and Jackson began to give orders at once to his officers. Long before daylight next morning, he was leading his troops through the forest toward Talledaga.

CHAPTER THIRTEEN

War Against the Red Sticks

GENERAL JACKSON paced back and forth in his tent. His arm, which was still in a sling, throbbed painfully. His stomach ached with hunger. Sitting on a low camp cot, his old friend John Coffee watched him with a worried frown.

"You'd better rest and save your strength, Andy," he remarked.

Andrew Jackson turned quickly.

"If supplies had come after we licked the Creeks at Talledaga, we could have wiped out the rest of Red Eagle's forces in ten days," he said hotly. "What's the matter with those people in Tennessee? I write, 'Send us bread! Send us meat! We are starving!' They promise us food. And nothing comes. The men are eating roots and acorns and—"

"And chewing on leather," John Coffee added. "Half the men in the army are determined to go home, Andy. Even you won't be able to hold them here much longer."

Jackson sighed impatiently. "I know it!" he exclaimed. "And you can't blame them. Men with empty stomachs don't make good soldiers. I'll tell the troops tomorrow that if supplies don't come within two days, I'll march them home to Tennessee. But I'm coming back again, John. I'm going to fight this war to a finish."

"And I'll be with you," said John Coffee.

Old Hickory smiled gratefully. The following morning he told his men what he had decided to do. Anxiously he watched and waited for supplies to arrive. But no wagon-train came creaking down the road within the next two days. Early on November 17th the army, with General Jackson in the lead, set out for Tennessee.

Although the men were hungry, most of

them were happy, for they were going home. They talked and sang as they rode or marched along under the cold gray sky. Suddenly there was a great commotion at the head of the line.

Scouts who were riding ahead had come back to report that they had met a wagon-train. It was loaded with flour and followed by one hundred and fifty cattle.

Quickly the officers shouted orders to break ranks. Within a short time the men were seated around blazing fires, stuffing themselves on half-cooked beef and bread. Then General Jackson gave the command to form ranks and return to Fort Strother.

Grumbling and muttering, the foot soldiers stepped into line. They were now well filled with food. But they knew that the flour and cattle which were left would not last them long. No one could guess when more supplies might arrive. And the men were tired of hunger, gnawing hunger that made them all feel sick and quarrelsome.

"Shoulder arms! March!"

The commands rang out along the line.

And the men marched—but one company did not march toward Fort Strother. With determined faces that company started on toward home. Other companies turned and followed. Distracted officers shouted to them to halt, to face about. Still the men kept marching ahead.

Andrew Jackson was sitting on his horse under a leafless tree with his aide, John Reid.

"That's mutiny!" he cried. Spurring his animal, he galloped after the men, seizing a musket from one as he passed him. Up to the head of the line he raced. Then he wheeled his horse around and faced the long line of soldiers. Colonel Coffee and Major Reid rode up beside him.

With his good arm, Jackson held the musket, resting the barrel on his horse's neck. His eyes flashed.

"I'll shoot the first man who takes another step forward!" he roared. "Cowards! Deserters! You're a disgrace to the state of Tennessee. You've eaten your fill. Turn about! Obey your officers. Go back to camp!"

The men stopped in their tracks. For a long

[*128*]

minute they looked at Old Hickory and he glared back at them. Then slowly they turned and marched the other way.

They were still grumbling, however, when they reached Fort Strother. That night some of them deserted. More followed next day. Soon General Jackson had only a hundred and thirty men left in camp.

To make matters worse, he learned that British troops were landing south of him, in

Florida. And that hundreds of Red Eagle's warriors were gathering at Horseshoe Bend on the Tallapoosa River, planning to attack Fort Strother. Then, when things looked blackest, he received a letter from Governor Blount, advising him to abandon the fort and return to Tennessee.

Many a commander in such a tight spot might have welcomed such a letter. But not Andy Jackson!

"I'll never do it," he told John Coffee. "If we don't wipe out Red Eagle's men, they'll join forces with the British and this country will run with blood. I'll die, John, rather than retreat."

Sitting down at once at his table, he picked up his pen and wrote a fiery letter to the Governor, refusing to abandon Fort Strother. He explained why. And he demanded more troops to fight against the Creeks.

To his surprise, the Governor sent him the troops. Jackson and his army then set out at once for Horseshoe Bend, seventy miles to the south.

Most of the men in this army were not trained soldiers. They were farmers, lawyers, blacksmiths, saddlers, teachers, and storekeepers. Yet they fought back bravely when the Red Sticks fell on their camp one night, and they drove the Indians off. Two days later, however, the Creeks attacked them as they were marching through the woods. And many of Jackson's men turned and ran.

Then Andrew Jackson was everywhere at once! Bullets and arrows whizzed around him as he plunged into the thick of battle, shouting at the fleeing men to return, and urging others to fight. They fought so furiously that the Creeks retreated into the woods, leaving their dead behind them.

Several hundred of Red Eagle's warriors were killed or wounded in these two battles. At last, on a day late in March, Andrew Jackson and his army of two thousand men reached the Creek village at Horseshoe Bend.

The Horseshoe was a thickly wooded peninsula, around which the Tallapoosa River curved. Across the neck of the peninsula the

[*131*]

Creeks had built a strong rampart of logs. Now nearly nine hundred warriors were gathered behind that rampart, eager for battle.

"Yah! Yah!" they yelled at the white men. "Come, fight! Hi-yi! Hi-yi! Hi-yi! Come, fight!"

Jackson and his army needed no urging. Already the General had sent Colonel Coffee with his cavalry to the other side of the river, to prevent any Red Sticks from escaping into the woods.

Now he signaled to his cannoneers. The two little brass cannon which he had brought from Fort Strother boomed, and the smoking balls buried themselves in the rampart. From behind the thick log walls came the high, shrill scream of a frightened child. Jackson shouted for a messenger.

"Go and tell the Creeks to send their women and children across the river where they'll be safe," he commanded. "We make war only on men."

The messenger galloped off. Soon the river was filled with canoes loaded with squaws and their children. When the last canoe had crossed the river safely, Jackson gave the command for the infantry to attack.

"Br-r-r-r-r-r-r-m!" sounded the drums. And the foot soldiers raced forward to storm the rampart.

The first man to scale the log wall was young Sam Houston. Waving his sword and shouting, he jumped down among the Indians. Other men followed him quickly.

With terrifying war whoops, the Indians attacked them, shooting from the underbrush, and from behind trees and log piles. The air was filled with flying spears and arrows, the zing of bullets and the cries of the wounded. Here and there among the fighters, Indian medicine men loudly chanted prayers to the Great Spirit for victory.

But the Indians were outnumbered. Jackson saw that they would soon all be killed. Hastily he sent another messenger to one of their chiefs, offering safety to all who would surrender.

The Red Sticks shot at the messenger as he

[*133*]

ran back, and went on fighting. The battle continued until dusk. When it was over, all but a few of the Indians were dead. The power of the Creeks had been broken. Now they would never be able to help the British. And the settlers of the Mississippi Territory could live in peace.

It was a great victory, but Andrew Jackson was too weary to rejoice. Forty-nine of his own men, including some of the friendly Indians, had been killed. A hundred and fifty-seven had been wounded.

The wounded were cared for. The dead were buried. And Jackson pushed further south. For he had not yet found Red Eagle— the man with a white father and an Indian mother, who was chief of all the Creeks.

An abandoned fort stood where the Coosa and the Tallapoosa rivers meet. General Jackson stopped there. The American flag was raised. And the soldiers gave the place a new name—Fort Jackson.

Then the General sent scouts out through the countryside to look for Red Eagle, with orders to bring him back in chains.

One day soon after this, a tall, light-colored Indian in worn moccasins and leather breeches came to the fort and asked to see General Jackson. The General looked at him in astonishment. For the man was Red Eagle himself.

The Indian chief stood before the white leader with his head held high.

"General Jackson," he said slowly, "I have come to give myself up. I can fight you no longer. I have done you much harm and I should have done you more. But my warriors are dead. I have nothing to ask for myself. But I beg you to send for the women and children of the war party, who are in the woods without

Red Eagle agreed that his people would keep the
peace and the two men shook hands

even an ear of corn. They never did any harm. But kill me, if the white people want it done."

Andrew Jackson shook his head. He could not kill this brave man who had walked unarmed into his camp and surrendered.

"I'll help the women and children," he replied. "You see that your people keep peace."

Red Eagle agreed to this and the two men shook hands. Then the tall chief strode from the fort and disappeared into the woods.

Now Andrew Jackson's work in the Creek country was finished. Before long he and his army were on their way home. And what a joyful journey that was!

Hundreds of men, women, and children lined the road leading into Nashville, cheering and shouting words of greeting to Old Hickory and his men. A splendid banquet was given in the General's honor, and he was presented with a handsome sword.

When he reached the Hermitage, friends and neighbors flocked to the plantation to welcome him. Rachel Jackson's eyes shone with pride as she watched him with his guests. But she was worried, for he looked thinner than ever, and very tired.

"Will you stay home now and rest?" she begged him when they were alone together. "You've been gone so long. Promise me that you'll stay home with little Andrew and Lincoyer and me."

But Andrew Jackson could not make such a promise. The war against the British was going badly. An English fleet was anchored off Pensacola in Florida. That town was full of English soldiers. Jackson felt sure that they would soon try to invade Louisiana and to capture the important city of New Orleans.

So off he rode again to the south, at the head of his men, determined to fight his old enemy —the redcoats—as hard as he had fought the Creeks.

CHAPTER FOURTEEN

The Night Battle

IT WAS the first of December. The wind was chilly in New Orleans and the sky was dark with rain clouds. In one of the narrow streets a large crowd of people had gathered before a big house with an upper balcony. They were waiting for their first sight of General Jackson, who had just arrived in the city. And they were talking uneasily.

Some spoke fearfully about the rumor that a British ship had been seen in near-by waters. Others talked about Andrew Jackson.

"He comes to help us defend our homes," one woman said, pulling her shawl up over her head. "But what can *he* do against the powerful British?"

"He chased them out of Pensacola," her husband reminded her.

"But New Orleans is different!" exclaimed an old man who stood beside him. "So big, with so many bayous and rivers all around and —look, there he is!"

He pointed to the balcony. A little group of men had just stepped out. One was the Governor of Louisiana. Another was the mayor of the city. And the third? Could that tall, gaunt, gray-haired man in the shabby blue cloak and dirty gray leather cap possibly be the great General Jackson?

There was a low murmur of disappointment in the crowd. But the Governor had begun to make a long speech, welcoming Jackson to New Orleans. The mayor followed this with another long speech. Then Jackson himself stepped to the balcony railing, erect and unsmiling.

"I pledge myself," he declared in a clear, ringing voice, "to protect this city, to drive your enemies into the sea, or to perish in the effort."

[*141*]

There were no murmurs of disappointment now. The crowd cheered wildly again and again. Here was a man who spoke out bravely as though he meant what he said. Here was a man other men could rally around. A leader.

"Jackson!" shouted the people. "Long live Jackson! Long live Old Hickory!"

Waving his hand to them, Jackson turned and walked quickly into the house. He knew that he must make plans to defend the city and he was anxious to begin at once.

Within a short time he was at the house on Royal Street which had been given him for his headquarters. There he pored over maps. He questioned citizens who came to offer their help. And he talked with engineers about where to build fortifications.

Late that night he turned to Colonel Livingston, who was one of his aides.

"New Orleans is going to be a difficult place to defend," he remarked. "If the British don't come up the Mississippi, they can sail into Lake Borgne from the Gulf of Mexico. Then, they can get at us in half a dozen different ways."

Colonel Livingston nodded and hitched his chair closer to the General's table. He had lived in New Orleans for many months and knew about the surrounding country.

"There's nothing but wild swamp land here, bordering the lake," he said, putting his finger on the map which lay before Jackson. "Miles of it—filled with tough reeds, six feet high. The only way the British could get through it and reach the plantations along the Mississippi would be to come along one of the bayous."

"Then we'll have the bayous blocked up with fallen trees and see that they are well guarded," Jackson said promptly. "We'll put gunboats on the lake to keep a watch for the enemy. We'll set up batteries of guns on the banks of the Mississippi, and we'll arm the two schooners that are anchored there."

He leaned back in his chair as the tall clock in the corner began to strike.

"Great heavens, it's midnight!" he exclaimed. "You'd better go to bed, Colonel."

"How about you, sir?" Colonel Livingston asked, getting to his feet.

Jackson laughed. "I'll get sleep when I need it," he promised.

But during the next two weeks he was almost too busy to sleep. Sometimes he worked at his headquarters. At other times he rode out to inspect the country and to plan new fortifications. One afternoon, as he was returning from such a trip, a messenger galloped up to him with his horse in a lather.

"Lake Borgne's filled with a big fleet of British ships!" he cried. "Our gunboats have all been destroyed!"

Jackson's heart sank. He had not expected the British so soon. Spurring his horse, he dashed toward the city. He reached his headquarters, dismounted, threw his reins to an orderly, and ran into the house. For thirty-six hours he worked without stopping for food or for rest.

Messengers galloped away from headquarters with orders for the troops who were guarding the city. "Resist the British as long as a man is left alive to point a gun."

Scouts sped north to find John Coffee, who

was on his way to New Orleans with his cavalry. And to give him Jackson's command: "You must not sleep until you reach me!"

Notices were posted in the streets of the city, forbidding anyone to leave it without permission. Ordering all street lamps put out at nine o'clock each night. Announcing that anyone found abroad after that time would be arrested as a spy.

The people were terrified when they learned that the enemy was so close. But they gained courage as they watched Andrew Jackson review the New Orleans militia in an open square called Place d'Armes.

"Jackson will save us," they told one another when the review was ended. And they cheered loudly as he rode away. "Jackson! Long live General Jackson!"

Though he bowed and smiled, Andrew Jackson hardly heard them. He was wondering where the British would strike. And how soon John Coffee and his cavalry would reach the city.

Coffee and his men came two days later.

The following morning another officer arrived with three thousand foot soldiers. Now Old Hickory felt easier in his mind than he had for some time. But he was tired—very tired.

Early in the afternoon two days before Christmas, he threw himself down on his sofa to rest for a few moments. Shutting his eyes, he thought longingly of Rachel and of little Andrew and of the peaceful Hermitage.

Suddenly there was a great commotion outside his room. Someone knocked, but before he could answer, the door was thrust open. Three men burst in, muddy, excited, and almost breathless. Jackson sprang to his feet.

"Gentlemen," he cried, "what news do you bring?"

"Important! Highly important!" **gasped**

one of the men. "The British have crossed the swamp. They've captured Major Villeré's plantation on the Mississippi River and—"

"Villeré's plantation!" Jackson broke in. "Then they're only eight miles from the city! By the Eternal, they'll not sleep on our soil. We'll fight them tonight!"

He strode to the door. So one bayou had been left open—unguarded! How? Why? But this was no time for questions. Loudly he called for his aides. As soon as they reached him he began to plan a surprise attack on the enemy, and to issue orders.

Two hours later he was riding hard, up the road along the Mississippi River. By five o'clock he and two thousand men were at Rodriguez Canal, only two miles from the place where the British army was making camp.

The sun sank and it grew dark quickly. A misty moon hung low in the sky. The British campfires blazed and flickered in the distance.

Whispered commands were passed along the lines. Slowly, silently, Jackson and his men pressed forward for some distance across a stubbly field. Then they halted.

Jackson turned in his saddle and looked anxiously toward the Mississippi. He had ordered the armed ship *Carolina* to float down the river, toward the British encampment. Yes, there she was—a dark shape drifting with the current.

At seven-thirty o'clock her guns would open fire on the British and he hoped that the enemy would rush forward. He planned to wait half an hour to let the redcoats believe that they had only the men on the ship to fight. Then he would order his cavalry and infantry to attack.

A cold gray fog was rising from the river. It blotted out the moon and dimmed the light from the enemy campfires. Jackson rode up and down the lines to see that the soldiers had plenty of ammunition. And to make sure that his two cannon were ready to be pulled into position.

He peered at his watch. Suddenly from down river there came a roar and through the fog he saw a burst of fire. The *Carolina* was doing her work! It was half past seven.

At eight his order was passed through the lines.

"Forward! Charge!"

Foot soldiers and cavalrymen rushed forward into the fog. The night was lighted with

the flash of their rifles. From the two American cannon came a steady "Boom! Boom! Boom!"

Though the British were taken completely by surprise, they fought back bravely. But the Americans continued to advance, except in one place! Jackson saw that the men near the cannon were retreating under steady

enemy fire. In a moment the redcoats would capture his only big guns.

Wheeling his horse around, Old Hickory galloped into the midst of the fight.

"Save the guns, boys!" he roared. "Save the guns!"

The retreating men rallied around him as bullets whistled past his head. A company of infantry rushed up and rescued the guns.

"Charge!" shouted Jackson, waving his sword. "Push on the bayonet! Fight, boys, *fight!*"

And they fought until at last the sound of British firing began to die away. The British were retreating. The battle had been won.

By midnight all the firing had ceased and the night was strangely still. The dead and wounded were brought in from the dark battlefield. The prisoners captured in the fight were questioned and marched off to New Orleans. And General Jackson ordered his men to return to the Rodriguez Canal.

Soon they were warming themselves beside blazing fires. But Andrew Jackson still sat on his horse, trying to peer through the night at the British camp. His scouts had reported that more British soldiers had landed and pushed through the swamp. Thousands of them!

"But they'll never get to New Orleans," he promised himself. "We'll build a mud rampart on this side of the canal. And we'll fight it out here until we drive every redcoat rascal into the river or the swamp."

CHAPTER FIFTEEN

The Hero of New Orleans

THE house near the Rodriguez Canal, which General Jackson was using as his headquarters, had been hit by a hundred British cannon balls. The windows were shattered. The January night was damp and cold.

In one of the rooms downstairs, Andrew Jackson shivered and turned restlessly on his couch. Near by, his four aides lay on the floor, snoring peacefully. But he could not sleep.

For two weeks he and his army had been at Rodriguez Canal. With the help of many of the citizens of New Orleans they had built a strong mud rampart behind the canal. Twice since Christmas they had been attacked there by the enemy. And twice they had beaten back the British after terrific fighting.

Now Jackson knew that the enemy was preparing for a much stronger attack. His spies had reported that the British army was larger than ever, and that every man in it was well armed.

"But with God's help, we'll smash them anyhow," Jackson promised himself.

He fumbled in the dark for his tinderbox. Striking a spark, he lighted a candle and looked at his watch. It was past one o'clock.

"Come, gentlemen," he said loudly to his aides. "We've slept long enough. The enemy may be upon us at any minute."

Still half-asleep, the four officers stumbled to their feet and buckled on their swords. Picking up their pistols, they followed the General out into the dark, foggy night.

The troops were already in their places behind the long rampart. They talked in low tones as they waited tensely for the battle to begin. Jackson went down the line to make sure that all was ready, and to encourage the men.

"I'll bet you fellows wish you were back in Tennessee," he remarked, as one group gathered around him.

"No," said half a dozen voices at once.

"Good boys!" Jackson exclaimed. "Stick to your guns now. Don't waste ammunition. You'll have to make every shot count."

"That's kind of hard to do when you can't see what you're shooting at," drawled a tall boy from Nashville. "Do you reckon this fog's ever going to lift, sir?"

"I hope so," the General replied. "Keep your spirits up!"

Clapping the boy on the shoulder, he walked on to the next group. There he warmed his hands over the embers of a dying fire and drank some of the coffee which the soldiers had made.

He was sick with indigestion, which had bothered him ever since the hungry days in the Red Sticks' country. For a week he had eaten little but rice. The hot coffee made him feel stronger. And he joked as he handed the empty cup to one of the men.

Then he glanced at the sky. It was growing lighter. But the fog still hung like a thick gray curtain between the rampart and the British camp. Anxiously he wondered what was going on behind that curtain, and when the enemy would strike.

At six o'clock he climbed to the top of the rampart with two of his officers. Peering through his telescope, he tried to see through the mist.

All at once there was a soft "Whisssssh!" A rocket sailed high over the British camp and burst in a shower of stars.

Jackson's heart began to pound, but he spoke calmly.

"That's their signal for an advance, I believe," he said. Then he cried out in surprise.

A sudden breeze had torn ragged holes in the curtain of fog. And there was the enemy, only six hundred yards away! Thousands of soldiers in scarlet coats and crossed white belts advancing rapidly, with gleaming bayonets, across the frosty field! Nearer they came—and "b-o-o-m!" went the first American cannon.

Riflemen sprang to their places on the firing step.

"Wait till they're closer!" Jackson sent the order down the line. "Aim above their belt plates! Ready! FIRE!"

Rifles cracked and scores of redcoats fell. But others came on, shooting as they ran forward. The first line of American riflemen moved back to reload and the second line stepped up quickly.

"Aim!" commanded the American officers. *"Fire!"*

Again the rifles blazed. More redcoats fell.

"Load!" shouted the American officers. "Aim! *Fire!*"

Bravely the British came on, stumbling over their wounded and dead, determined to capture the rampart. They were trained soldiers who had fought in many parts of the world. But never before had they been forced to meet such a steady hail of bullets.

"Load! Aim! *Fire!*" Again and again the command rang out, while Jackson strode calmly up and down the line, encouraging his men.

[*158*]

"That's it, boys! Give it to them! Steady, there! Let's finish this business up today!"

"Load! Aim! *Fire!*"

On and on went the firing until hundreds of red-coated officers and soldiers lay dead or dying on the field. On and on, until what was left of the British army had retreated.

Then General Jackson shouted, "Hold your fire!" For the battle had been won.

He had planned so carefully and commanded so well that only six of his men had been killed and seven wounded.

Soon the British were aboard their boats, preparing to leave Lake Borgne. But one of their officers, General Keene, had lost his sword in the fighting. He wrote to Andrew Jackson, saying that he hoped it might be returned to him.

It was found on the battlefield, several days later, and taken to General Jackson. He looked at it, and absent-mindedly he fingered an old scar on his head.

Suddenly there flashed through his mind the picture of another sword. A shining blade, held high by a scowling officer, over two boys

—himself and his brother, Rob. What had he said to Rob on that dreadful morning?

"Some day I'll meet the British in a *fair* fight!"

Well, now he had met them—and he had won. Never again, if he could help it, would a British officer have a chance to command an American boy to clean his boots.

The next morning he told a messenger to take General Keene's sword to its owner. Before long the British sailed away. And General Jackson and his troops marched back to New Orleans.

A splendid welcome awaited them there. The houses had been gaily decorated with flags and bunting. The streets were thronged with people, dressed in their best.

How they cheered when Jackson rode into Place d'Armes and dismounted! Church bells pealed and bands played "Yankee Doodle" as he walked under the arch of flowers which had been set up in his honor. Children, dressed in white, scattered blossoms in his path. And everyone who could, crowded after him into the Cathedral, to give thanks to God because New Orleans had been saved.

Meanwhile, hard-riding couriers were carrying the news north and east, throughout the country.

"New Orleans is safe! Jackson wins great victory!"

The war against the British had not been going well in other parts of the United States. How good it was now to hear about an American victory! People in many parts of the country, who had never heard of Old Hickory, began to question each other.

"Who is this man Jackson? Where does he come from? What is he like?"

In Nashville, men boasted proudly that they had always known Andy Jackson would do something big some day. And Rachel Jackson set out at once to join her husband in New Orleans.

On a mild day in February, General Jackson rode in his carriage to the dock to meet the keel-boat which was bringing his wife down the river. There it was coming slowly down the yellow Mississippi. And there, among the passengers at the railing, was Rachel, as plump and sweet as ever, with little Andrew clinging to her hand.

It seemed to the impatient General that the boat would never land. But at last he had Rachel in his arms, holding her so tightly that she gasped for breath.

"Let me look at you," she begged, stepping back and peering up into his face. "Oh, my dear, you're thinner than a toothpick. It's a good thing that I've come to look after you.

Andrew, aren't you going to speak to your papa?"

Five-year-old Andrew shook his head. He had not seen his father in seven months, and he drew back shyly when the tall man in the gold-trimmed blue uniform stooped to kiss him. But in ten minutes he was in the carriage, seated on Jackson's knee, and telling him

all about the keel-boat, the Hermitage, and Lincoyer.

Andrew Jackson had made many friends in New Orleans and they all wanted to meet his wife. She was invited to so many concerts, theater parties, and dinners that her head was in a whirl.

On Washington's birthday, she and her husband went to a magnificent ball which was given in their honor. As they rode home late in the evening, Mrs. Jackson leaned her head against her husband's shoulder.

"We've been so gay I had almost forgotten that the country is still at war," she said.

General Jackson smiled and patted her hand. "I've not forgotten," he told her.

And indeed he was busy every day, all day, planning what to do if the British should return. But they never came back. On the 13th of March a courier galloped into the city and pulled up his horse before Jackson's headquarters on Royal Street. He had ridden hard all the way from Washington with wonderful news.

The war was over! A treaty of peace had been signed in Holland by representatives from the United States and England on December 24th, 1814.

"Why, that was right after you fought the first battle at Rodriguez Canal!" Mrs. Jackson exclaimed to her husband. "If you'd known about the treaty you needn't have fought any more."

"But we didn't know," Andrew Jackson reminded her. "And perhaps it was a good thing that we didn't. I think at last we've proved to the English that the Americans are a strong free people who will never let their land be invaded by anyone."

Mrs. Jackson nodded soberly. Then she changed the subject.

"Now that the war is over, how soon can we go home?" she asked.

"Just as soon as I've disbanded my army and finished up my business here," her husband promised with a smile.

Nearly four weeks later, the Jacksons started for Nashville. Cheering crowds met

[165]

them in towns and villages along the way. In Nashville a great celebration was held to welcome the General. But the best welcome of all came when he reached the Hermitage.

There, in the soft May twilight, relatives and old friends were waiting on the steps of the big log house to greet him. The Donelson boys rushed forward to help their aunt and uncle from the carriage. Negro servants with beaming faces began to unload the baggage. Little Lincoyer threw himself into Mrs. Jackson's arms. Dogs barked joyfully. And everyone talked at once.

"Home is the most wonderful place in the world," Jackson told his wife, as they went up to bed late that night.

"Yes," agreed Mrs. Jackson. "And I hope you'll never have to leave it again."

But, of course, he did.

CHAPTER SIXTEEN

Joy Turns to Sorrow

Young ANDY JACKSON was tall for a boy of eleven. But not tall enough to see over the heads of the people who had gathered near the wharf at Nashville.

"After all, it's our mother and father that most of them have come to meet," he said to Lincoyer. "Let's get up in front."

Lincoyer agreed. He grasped the arm of little Andrew Hutchings, who had come to live with the Jacksons when his father died. And the three boys wriggled their way through the crowd until they stood close to the edge of the dock. Eagerly they watched the little steamboat which was puffing up the river, leaving a black ribbon of smoke against the pale November sky.

[*167*]

"Can you see them yet?" Lincoyer asked as the boat drew nearer.

"No! Not yet," Andy replied. "Thunderation! That old boat's slow!"

Lincoyer grinned. "It was a whole day late last time Papa came home from Florida," he said. "Remember?"

Andy nodded, thinking of the last trip his father had made to Florida. That country had belonged to Spain then. Indians from Florida had been raiding plantations across the border in Georgia, robbing and killing American planters. The Spanish governor had not seemed able to stop them. So the President of the United States had asked Andrew Jackson to do so.

At the head of a small army, General Jackson had marched into Florida and settled the trouble quickly. Then he had come home, bringing Spanish saddles for Andy and Lincoyer, and other gifts for the rest of the family.

Since that time Florida had been bought by the United States. And Jackson had been asked to be the first governor of the new territory. So again he had gone south, taking Mrs. Jackson with him.

"And they've been away seven months," Andy thought, peering at the men and women who stood on the deck of the approaching steamboat. "I'll bet—"

Suddenly he waved his arm. "Hey, Ma!" he yelled excitedly. "Papa!"

The tall gray-haired man and the plump little woman who stood near the railing waved back. Then someone in the crowd cried, "There's Old Hickory! There's the General! Come on, give a cheer for Jackson!"

The crowd cheered and the tall man waved again. When the boat was made fast to the wharf, he and his wife were the first passengers to walk down the gangplank. Before the boys could do more than say "hello," General and Mrs. Jackson were surrounded by people, eager to greet them.

At last one of the Negro dock hands yelled, "Make way there, gentlemen! Please make way! Here comes the General's carriage!"

The fine coach which Jackson had taken

with him to Florida was rolled ashore. Then four prancing white horses were led down the gangplank and quickly harnessed. The coachman took his place. The General helped his wife into the carriage and sat down beside her. Andy, Lincoyer, and Andrew mounted the horses which they had ridden to Nashville. And the Jacksons started off for the Hermitage.

The crowd roared good-by as the coach rattled away up the road from the river. Soon the little party was turning into a wide curved driveway.

It did not lead to the old blockhouse. It led to the big new home of red brick which Andrew Jackson had built for his wife two years earlier. A home surrounded by tall trees, wide lawns, and beautiful gardens.

Mrs. Jackson loved this new Hermitage. As she alighted from the coach she saw that her flower gardens had been neglected. The next morning, as soon as the boys had left for school, she went outside to pull weeds and to transplant bulbs.

In the library, Andrew Jackson emptied out a sackful of mail and sat down before a cheerful fire to read his letters. To his surprise, scores of people had written to him saying that they thought he should be the next president of the United States.

"I never heard of such foolishness!" he exclaimed to Rachel that evening, as they walked through the garden together. "I may be good at commanding troops in a rough sort of way, but I'm not fit to be President."

"Oh, yes, you are!" Rachel Jackson declared quickly. "But you've done your share for the country, Andrew. I think people ought to forget about you for a while now and let you stay here quietly with me."

"So do I," Jackson said, patting her shoulder.

But people are not likely to forget a man as

famous as the hero of New Orleans. Thousans of Americans loved Jackson and trusted him and wanted him as the leader of their country. They urged him so strongly to run for president that at last he decided he must do so.

Mrs. Jackson sighed unhappily when her husband told her of this decision. "You'll be

so busy now that I'll never see you," she said forlornly. "And I shall hate living in that huge palace they call the White House."

Andrew Jackson laughed. "Don't fret about that!" he exclaimed. "I haven't been elected yet."

"You will be," Mrs. Jackson assured him.

But she was wrong. When election time came around, a gentleman from Massachusetts, named John Quincy Adams, was made the president.

The race had been a close one, however. Hundreds of thousands of people had voted for Old Hickory. They were bitterly disappointed because he had not won. Jackson decided that he would run again at the next election, four years later. So in 1828 he did and he was elected to the highest office in the land.

Then what rejoicing there was throughout the country! People gathered around huge bonfires, cheering for Old Hickory. They held barbecues and noisy parades.

From the towns and villages of Tennessee,

men and women flocked to the Hermitage to congratulate Andrew and Rachel Jackson. And plans were made to hold a big banquet and ball in their honor, at the Nashville Inn on the twenty-third of December.

But the banquet and ball were never held. For Rachel Jackson suddenly became very ill. Doctors could do little to help her. Two days before Christmas, she died.

She had been dearly loved throughout the countryside, and the hearts of thousands of people were filled with sorrow. As for poor Andrew Jackson, he could not believe that his wife was gone. Hour after hour he sat with his head in his hands, remembering the happy times they had had together. And trying to picture what life would be like without his Rachel.

After her funeral, he longed to be alone with his grief. But the people of the United States had made him their leader, and he could not fail them. Heartbroken and lonely, he left the Hermitage and began his long journey to Washington to take up his duties as President.

CHAPTER SEVENTEEN

President Andrew Jackson

IT WAS Inauguration Day—March 4th, 1829. The sun shone brightly on Washington, melting the snow which had fallen during the night. A vast crowd of people had gathered on the muddy west lawn of the Capitol. And nearly every seat on the roped-off portico was filled.

In one of the seats near the front, a richly dressed old lady turned to speak to her companion.

"My dear, just see that mob!" she exclaimed. "This city's been filled with dreadful, common-looking people ever since Jackson came. They're all friends of his, no doubt. He may be a famous general, but he's just a

[*176*]

brawling backwoods lawyer, after all. Have you seen him yet?"

"No," replied Miss Bascom, "I—"

"Well, I haven't either," Mrs. Smith rattled on. "But I've seen every President before him. Every one of them was a well-educated man from a fine Eastern family. Now this rough old soldier from the West is—"

"Shh!" Miss Bascom hushed her sharply. "There he is."

At that moment there was a long loud cheer from the thousands of people on the big lawn.

"Jackson! Hey, Old Hickory! We're all with you, Andy! Jackson! Jackson! Jackson!"

Tall and dignified, with the sun shining on his thick white hair, Andrew Jackson bowed again and again. Still the cheering went on.

Old Mrs. Smith leaned once more toward Miss Bascom.

"My dear," she whispered, "he's really quite noble looking. Why, he seems to be a gentleman! I'm surprised. Aren't you?"

Miss Bascom did not reply. She was trying to hear Andrew Jackson, who had just began to speak to the crowd. When Jackson had finished his speech, he laid his hand on the open Bible which the Chief Justice held out to him.

"I do solemnly swear," he said, "that I will faithfully execute the office of the President of the United States, and will, to the best of my ability, preserve, protect, and defend the Constitution of the United States."

Raising the Bible to his lips, he kissed it. Again the crowd cheered wildly. And cannon boomed to salute the newly made President.

With a quick smile at Major Jack Donelson, who had come to Washington with him, President Jackson left the portico. Mounting his horse, he started riding up the wide avenue that led to the White House.

The crowd followed him in handsome carriages, in rickety farm wagons, on horseback, and on foot. Rich and poor alike, all were bound for the grand White House reception.

Until this time, only people who were used to fine society had been invited to such receptions. But Andrew Jackson had ordered that anyone who wished to come should be admitted.

Hundreds of people flocked through the gates and thronged into the beautiful East Room. Many of them did not know how to behave in such splendid surroundings. They jostled and shoved, grabbing for cakes and plates of ice cream. They upset furniture and broke dishes as they surged forward to shake the hand of the new President. In muddy boots they climbed up on the damask-covered chairs, craning their necks to see their hero.

It was late when the reception was ended. And President Jackson was exhausted. That night he lay in bed thinking about the important work that lay before him.

Already Congressman and other officials had sought him out to tell him how they thought he should run the government. And whom they thought he should appoint to help him. He had listened to them politely.

"And I'll keep on listening to men who come with advice," he told himself. "But in the end I shall make up my own mind as to what is right, and govern the country in the way that seems best to me."

He missed Rachel sorely, although he had little time to be lonely. Many old friends came to see him in Washington. Jack Donelson and his wife and children lived with him in the White House. And frequently young Andrew junior brought his pretty wife and baby daughter from the Hermitage for long visits.

Jackson loved all the children and spent as many hours with them as he could. Important visitors were likely to find him with one of the younger children on his knee. He worried if any of them so much as sneezed. And often, late at night, he got out of bed, lighted his candle, and went to their nursery to see that they were all right.

Meanwhile, President Jackson was doing the best he could to manage the affairs of the nation wisely. Although he made mistakes, as all men do, he governed the country so well for four years that the people elected him to serve a second term. And when, four years later, the time drew near for him to leave

Washington, hundreds of men and women flocked to the White House bringing him gifts.

On March 4, 1837, Mr. Martin Van Buren was inaugurated as the eighth President of the United States. Then Andrew Jackson was free to return to the Hermitage.

Friends gathered around him as he left the White House two days later and climbed into his coach. People lined the streets to watch him drive away. And when he reached the little railroad depot he found that thousands had gathered there to say good-by.

Slowly Old Hickory climbed aboard the little train which was to carry him to the end of the railway line, in Maryland, where a coach and horses were waiting for him. Stepping out on the platform of the last car, he faced the quiet crowd. Tears streamed down the faces of the women. Men wiped their eyes and removed their hats in honor of a great general, a great president, and a great man whom they all loved.

The conductor rang his bell. There was a

hiss of steam. The train started up with a jerk and puffed away down the track. As it rounded a curve, Jackson waved farewell to the people.

Then, with a little smile, he turned and stepped inside the car. He had served his country well for many years. Now, at last, he was going back to the Hermitage to stay.

SIGNATURE BOOKS are the true life-stories of real boys and girls who grew up to be famous men and women. These books tell of the many exciting adventures of those boys and girls when they were growing up, and what they did to make themselves remembered.

Leading authors and artists have worked together to give you the thrilling stories of these interesting people. If you liked the story you have just read, you will enjoy reading the books listed below and on the next page.

SIGNATURE BOOKS
"Names that Made History"

ENID LAMONTE MEADOWCROFT, *Supervising Editor*

THE STORY OF ULYSSES S. GRANT
By Jeannette Covert Nolan.   *Illustrated by Lynd Ward*

THE STORY OF ANDREW JACKSON
By Enid LaMonte Meadowcroft.   *Illustrated by David*
                                                                    Hendrickson

THE STORY OF LAFAYETTE
By Hazel Wilson.   *Illustrated by Edy Legrand*

THE STORY OF ROBERT E. LEE
By Iris Vinton.   *Illustrated by John Alan Maxwell*

THE STORY OF ABRAHAM LINCOLN
By Nina Brown Baker.   *Illustrated by Warren Baumgartner*

THE STORY OF FLORENCE NIGHTINGALE
By Margaret Leighton.   *Illustrated by Corinne B. Dillon*

THE STORY OF LOUIS PASTEUR
By Alida Sims Malkus.   *Illustrated by Jo Spier*

THE STORY OF THEODORE ROOSEVELT
By Winthrop Neilson.   *Illustrated by Edward A. Wilson*

THE STORY OF GEORGE WASHINGTON
By Enid LaMonte Meadowcroft. *Illustrated by Edward A. Wilson*

HANDSOME BOOKPLATES

*If you would like a set of bookplates, so that you can write
your own name in these books just the way the great signa-
tures are shown, send your name and address to*
SIGNATURE BOOKS, GROSSET & DUNLAP, INC.,
1107 BROADWAY, NEW YORK 10, N. Y.
*We will mail you, upon receipt of ten cents to pay the cost of
postage and handling, a set of handsomely designed
bookplates, each one different.*